# EXPLORING THE NEW RIVER

S.<sup>r</sup> HUGH MYDDELTON Knight & Baronet.

# EXPLORING THE NEW RIVER

Michael Essex-Lopresti

K.A.F. BREWIN BOOKS
STUDLEY 1988

Published by
K.A.F. Brewin Books, Studley, Warwickshire
September 1986
Reprinted (with amendments) April 1987
Second Edition 1988
Reprinted March 1990
Reprinted June 1992
Reprinted January 1995

ISBN 0 947731 49 0

Typeset in Press Roman and
made and printed in Great Britain
by Supaprint (Redditch) Ltd., Redditch, Worcs.

To Lorna, my wife

# CONTENTS

# LIST OF ILLUSTRATIONS

## INTRODUCTION TO THE FIRST EDITION

Some years ago my wife and I were cruising up the River Lee Navigation when we read in the British Waterways Inland Cruising Booklet that Great Amwell, near Hardmead Lock, was worth visiting. We moored near a footbridge and crossed a watercourse which continued southwards alongside the road past a pumping station. Here we were told something of the New River which is neither new nor a river; it is a man-made channel which has been supplying London with fresh water for nearly four hundred years. Continuing our cruise we noticed the Intake House as we approached Hertford Lock, so on reaching Hertford we decided to buy a booklet on the New River as our curiosity had been aroused. But our search was fruitless; nowhere could we find any guide to exploring the New River and, as far as I can discover, none exists. If I wanted to know more about the enterprise I would have to seek it myself and that is what I have done in the past dozen years. This led to requests for talks on the subject and from these the idea for a book arose.

This, then, is the handbook for which we were searching when first we stumbled on the New River. It is not intended to be a scholarly treatise on the history of the project and its social influence, though the wealth of material I have gathered indicates that such a volume would be justified. I have had to exclude much of it to keep the size of the handbook manageable and I have contented myself with providing references and a bibliography where additional information can be found. My aim has been to produce a pocket guide for those interested in exploring the New River. I have included a brief history of the undertaking; this is both fascinating and necessary for an understanding of the features to be seen along its course. The description of the present course and of remnants of the old loops will serve as a guide for those interested in visiting this outstanding example of industrial archaeology, which is still fulfilling the function for which it was built nearly four centuries ago.

Michael Essex-Lopresti
June, 1986

## INTRODUCTION TO THE SECOND EDITION

So many people have written to me, since the book was published, sending to me – or drawing to my attention – documents and items of interest relating to the history of the New River that I have gathered a lot of new material. Further I have delved deeper into some of the engineering features of the past, and as proposals for the future of the southern-most section evolve it seemed appropriate to prepare an updated version of the book.

I have taken the opportunity of revising the headings in the historical part of the book, adding a new chapter on the financial arrangements devised to pay for the enterprise and I have included some more illustrations. More old books which mention the New River have been consulted and I have quoted from some of them so the list of references is greatly extended (the new entries appear from reference 26). I have also noted where footpaths are becoming overgrown; following the storm in October 1987 a number of trees brought down have not yet been fully cleared.

Discussions on the future of the part of the New River no longer needed by Thames Water Authority continue; the paragraphs relating to this have been brought up to date and represent the position at the time of writing.

Michael Essex-Lopresti
June, 1988

# A BRIEF HISTORY OF THE NEW RIVER

## 1.    16th Century London and its Water Supply

During the reign of Queen Elizabeth I (1558-1603) the population of London reached about 180,000 (1), living in houses which extended slightly beyond the city walls and in an area south of London Bridge where William Shakespeare was presenting his new plays at the Globe theatre.    In addition the centre of Court and Government was upstream at Westminster, linked to the City by a highway through the village of Charing.    Although London had plenty of water from the Thames and its many tributaries, the public preferred to use this flowing water to carry away its refuse and sewage.    The need for a supply of fresh water for domestic purposes had long been recognised.    Since 1236 a six-inch lead pipe, which had been authorised by Henry III, had been conveying water from six wells in the neighbourhood of Tyburn to conduits in various parts of the city.    New conduits were built notably in West Cheap (Cheapside) in 1285, in Fleet Street, Aldermanbury and Cripplegate in 1438, in Aldgate in 1535 and in Holborn in 1577.    Altogether sixteen conduits carried a limited amount of fresh water into London.    We are told that "notwithstanding the number of conduits was considerable, they were found insufficient, and many citizens were obliged to fetch their water from the Thames.    In those times, persons were regularly employed to convey water from the river, or the conduits, to the houses which they did in vessels, called tankards, that held about three gallons.    They were hooped round, like a pail, and were, in figure, like the frustrum of a cone.    They had a small iron handle at the upper end, like an alehouse pot, and, being fitted with a bung or stopple, were easily portable." (2)  (see page 17).    There were several wells but these were privately owned and of shallow depth so they too soon became polluted (35).

Water Bearer

In 1570, Matthews tells us, the "Corporation of London obtained an Act of Parliament to empower them to cut a river for conveying water to the City from any part of Middlesex, or Hertfordshire; and ten years was the time specified for the execution of the plan" (26). This area is bounded by the Rivers Colne, Lee and Thames and the one hundred foot contour line runs from the Colne Valley, south of Uxbridge, to west and north London, then accompanying the Lee Valley up to Hertford (Map 1). The water supply was needed on the high ground in north London so

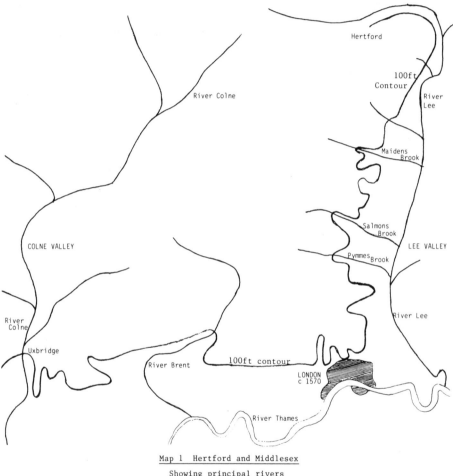

Map 1   Hertford and Middlesex

Showing principal rivers
and 100ft contour

that it could be distributed by gravity to houses in the City. As nothing happened within the decade, the Act lapsed, and in 1582 a Dutchman, Peter Morris (or Morice) was granted a five-hundred year lease to build a tidal pump under an arch of London Bridge "for conveying water into the houses of the inhabitants of the city, and for the better service of the city in case of casualty by fire" (3). Morris was required to pay ten shillings yearly to the city and two years later he acquired the right to use a second arch. It is ironical that in 1666 the Fire of London, which started just north of

2

London Bridge, destroyed the waterwheels at the outset "so that the water system with its pumps could no longer be used to stay the fire" (see page 18). Reconstruction was authorised the following year and in 1701 the London Bridge Waterworks Company successfully negotiated the rights for a further two arches. A steam engine was added in 1762 to supplement the tidal pump. However, as the wheels were becoming a navigation hazard, the 1822 Act abolished them (see page 19) and transferred the water responsibility to the New River Company. The old London Bridge itself was replaced in 1831 (27). Thames Water Authority as successor to the Metropolitan Water Board which, in turn, took over from the New River Company, will continue to pay annuities until the 500-year lease lapses in the year 2082.

## 2.  The Plans for a New River

In 1580 Russell proposed a channel from the 'River at Uxbridge' — the Colne — to the upper end of Holborn (26) along the 100ft contour. In all the references to this scheme (for instance Matthews 1835, Berry 1957, Gough 1964) nowhere can I find a first name or initial for 'Russell'. Although his proposal was never undertaken, the same course was chosen for the Paddington Arm of the Grand Junction Canal over two centuries later.

About 1600 Edmund Colthurst proposed a similar channel from the springs of Amwell and Chadwell near Hertford to Islington, again using the 100ft contour. To make the plan more attractive he offered to supply two-thirds of the water for cleaning town ditches and the remainder to houses in the cities of Westminster and London (4). As the scheme had the approval of Elizabeth I and the Corporation of the City of London, the acquisition of land was being considered but the Queen died before Colthurst was granted the Licence to proceed. Letters Patent dated 18 April, 1604, were issued by King James I authorising Colthurst to dig a river, not more than six feet wide, within seven years; the following year Colthurst claimed that he had dug three miles at a cost of £200 and he applied to the City Corporation for financial support. As there were rival proposals, the Common Council set up a Committee to promote a Parliamentary Bill to bring water from Uxbridge, the Lee or from Amwell. Colthurst protested in view of the work he had already undertaken and although the Act which reached the Statute Book on 20 May, 1606 was "An Acte for the Bringing in a freshe Streame of Running Water to the Northe parts of the City of London", the preamble recorded the advantages of a "New River for bringing Water to London from Chadwell and Amwell in Hertfordshire" — Colthurst's scheme. However the Act enlarged the width of the channel to ten feet.

The Corporation was unwilling to bear the financial risk itself, and it seemed unhappy about Colthurst's resources. However, noting that he had 'taken unto him persons of good sufficiencie' as partners, the Corporation made Colthurst responsible for the project, provided that he expected no money from the City and that he completed it in two years (28). Colthurst accepted this on condition that he and his partners received all the profits. Although this was approved by the Common Council on 14 March, 1609, just two weeks later the same body accepted an offer from Hugh Myddelton, a London goldsmith who had been a Member of Parliament, to pay for and complete the work in four years. It is probable that Myddelton was one of the 'persons of good sufficiencie' whom Colthurst had taken into partnership but evidently the Corporation preferred to invest the City's powers in a man of substance. Consequently Myddelton's name has become identified with the New River. This is sad because it was Colthurst who first proposed the scheme, planned it, even began

3

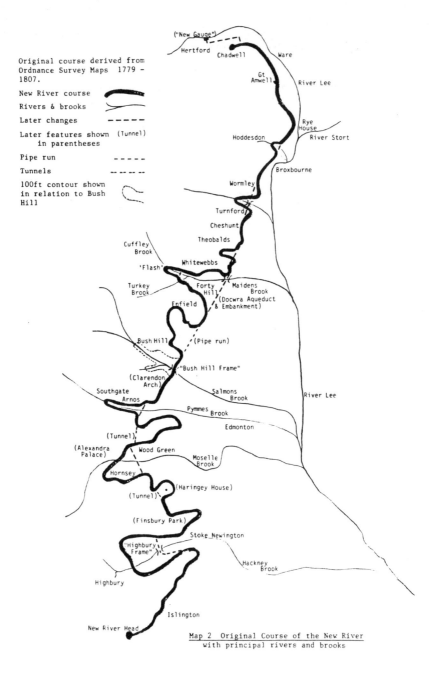

Original course derived from
Ordnance Survey Maps 1779 –
1807.

New River course

Rivers & brooks

Later changes

Later features shown (Tunnel)
in parentheses

Pipe run

Tunnels

100ft contour shown
in relation to Bush
Hill

("New Gauge")

Hertford    Chadwell        Ware

Gt
Amwell              River Lee

Rye
House
Hoddesdon              River Stort

Broxbourne

Wormley

Turnford

Cheshunt

Cuffley        Theobalds
Brook

'Flash'    Whitewebbs

Turkey         Forty    Maidens
Brook          Hill     Brook
                        (Docwra Aqueduct
Enfield                 & Embankment)

Bush Hill      (Pipe run)

"Bush Hill Frame"
(Clarendon
Arch)
Southgate              Salmons
Arnos                  Brook        River Lee

Pymmes Brook

Edmonton

(Tunnel)
(Alexandra
Palace)    Wood Green
                    Moselle
Hornsey             Brook

(Haringey House)
(Tunnel)

(Finsbury Park)

Stoke Newington
"Highbury
Frame"
Hackney
Brook
Highbury

Islington
New River Head

Map 2  Original Course of the New River
with principal rivers and brooks

4

working on it at his own expense and was certainly engaged in its construction (28) but his name is no longer associated with the enterprise and there is no statue, monument, nor even a road in London named after him today.

Much of our knowledge of the construction of the New River derives from the painstaking analysis by G.C.F. Berry (4) of nine accounts books which record all payments "for the bringinge of watter from the springs of Chadwell and Amwell to the Citty of london", between 20 February 1609 and 30 September, 1632. They show that Hugh Myddelton, in whose hand the first entries are written, was working with Colthurst before the Common Council accepted his offer to finance and complete the work. We see that Colthurst was re-imbursed for expenses on 20 February 1609 and he was paid regular wages from 5 May 1609 until August 1616, with the exception of a break between 16 June 1610 and 12 October 1611 when construction work was suspended (see below). Regular payments were also made to Mr. Wright for surveying the course. Edward Wright of Norfolk was an eminent mathematician who was associated with charts and with the Mercator projection used in maps, and it was he, no doubt, who achieved the extraordinary accuracy which we now find difficult to believe possible in the early 17th century.

## 3.    Building the New River

Several dates are suggested for the start of construction. Colthurst had started, at his own expense, to cut a channel from chadwell Spring in 1605, but Morris states that the first sod was cut at Chadwell on 21 April, 1609 (1) while Berry notes that the first wage payment to Colthurst was on 5 May, 1609 (4), a date confirmed by Gough for on the same day £2.18s was paid for the delivery of supplies (28). Percy (2) states that work began on 28 February, 1608 but this can be attributed to a mis-reading of the accounts book; that was the date on which the book was begun when payments were incurred for legal charges. The inscription on the monument at Chadwell records "Opened 1608", the year quoted by Charles Dickens in his London Guide (see page 23), and an issue of the Boy's Own Paper dated Saturday 21 March 1885 states "on the 20th April, 1608, the work commenced" (29). Professor Rudden (34) has pointed out to me that the apparent discrepancy in years is explained by the fact that in 1752 the New Year was changed from 25 March to 1 January. Consequently all the dates quoted, with the exception of that in the Boys Own Paper, are close; 28 February, 1608 was only a few weeks before 21 April, 1609.

The date of its completion – 29 September, 1613 – is well documented.

By following the 100ft contour, the course was far from straight, usually passing up one side of a valley and back down the other. Thus the twenty-four miles from Hertford to London were traversed by a man-made channel of about forty miles in length, ten feet wide and approximately four feet deep, made waterproof with puddled clay.

From Chadwell Spring the New River was dug on the 100ft contour on the west side of the Lee Valley. Several large brooks flowing towards the River Lee crossed its route in small valleys so that, to remain on the same level, the channel had to be diverted westwards in loops and small hills had to be circumvented. Initially the New River lies close to the River Lee but the level of the Lee drops substantially through some seventeen locks and the New River course swings westwards away from it.

During its construction up to six hundred labourers were said to be employed, each receiving half-a-crown a day (1), though other sources quote different figures (5). The channel was cut eastwards and southwards following the bend of the River Lee past Hoddesdon and Broxbourne when work came to a standstill while negotiations continued.   The reason frequently quoted for this stoppage was that on reaching Theobalds Park, north of Enfield, Myddelton ran out of money;  he approached James I whose Palace was in Theobalds and the King agreed to put up half the money on condition that he would receive half of the profits (5).   However Berry concluded that work stopped when the channel had reached Wormley, north of Cheshunt, because of opposition by landowners to the acquisition of land needed for the first of the great loops to take the New River round a valley (4).   The King became involved when the City appealed to the Lords of the Privy Council in April, 1610, to be "mediators to the Kings most excellent Maiesty that all lette and hindraunce may be removed and way given to Mr. Midleton".

The House of Commons — said to be composed mainly of country gentlemen — did not support Myddelton and after a delay of more than a year the King, urgently seeking new sources of revenue, offered to become a partner in the project, putting up half the money for the entire enterprise, and allowed the New River to be cut through the Royal estates at Theobalds free of charge.   Incidentally, at this time a warrant was obtained "to bringe a seditious fellowe . . . who persuaded ye water bearers of London to petition his Maiestie against ye newe Ryver" before Sir Henry Montague, the Recorder — another source of opposition to the project. (4)

Myddelton's Glory, engraved by G. Bickham, 1772.  "Lord Mayor, Sir John Swinnerton, Kt., on a white palfry, pointing exultantly to Sir Hugh, with the Recorder, Sir John Montague, afterwards Lord Keeper and Earl of Manchester, and by his side Sir Thomas Myddelton, Hugh Myddelton's elder brother, who was chosen as Lord Mayor on the day." (12)

Construction continued in a south-westerly direction and through Theobalds Park on level ground, but beyond this a major diversion occurred at Maidens Brook north of Enfield Chase. Remaining on the one-hundred foot contour the channel made a three and a half mile detour westwards through Whitewebbs Park to Crews Hill. Here it was at a lower level than Cuffley Brook — which flows into Maidens Brook — and a wooden trough carried the brook over the New River. It is suggested that the reason for this is that Cuffley Brook could be tapped for additional water by means of a 'flash' when needed (6); the lane approaching this area is still called "Flash Lane". On its return to the Lee Valley, the New River skirted south of Forty Hill so it rejoined the straight route about a mile south of Maidens Brook.

On reaching the high ground at Enfield a large loop — the horseshoe loop — was built round the town but no such diversion was made at Salmons Brook, Bush Hill. Instead the New River was carried across the valley in a 666ft lead trough on a timber frame which reached a height of 24 feet. Below Southgate a two mile westerly loop in Arnos Park carried the New River over Pymmes Brook and the high ground in Wood Green was skirted by an eastward loop towards Tottenham. There were similar diversions in Hornsey and Harringay and the channel ended at New River Head in the round pond near Sadlers Wells.

Although the distance from Hertford to Islington is only twenty-four miles, the actual course of the New River was nearly forty miles when it was built; throughout its length there was a gentle gradient to promote the flow of the water and the total fall in the level was only eighteen feet, an average of five and a half inches a mile. One hundred and fifty seven bridges had to be built to carry roads and footpaths over the flowing water.

The need to avoid pollution of the water was recognised from the start and an indenture dated 1612 included "Wee doe by these presents for us our heirs and Successors straightly charge and comaund all pson and psons whatsoever That they or anie of them doe not hereafter cast or putt into the said new river anie earth rubbish soyle gravell stones doggs catts or anie Cattle Carrion or anie unwholesome or uncleane thing nor shall wash nor clense anie clothes wooll or other thinge in the said river".

The New River was ceremonially opened on 29 September, 1613, by the Lord Mayor of London, Sir John Swinnerton, in the presence of the Lord Mayor elect, Sir Thomas Myddelton, Hugh's brother. The water was distributed to houses in London by means of wooden pipes, made of hollowed out elm trunks with an internal diameter of up to seven inches; one end of each pipe was sharpened, rather like a pencil, and inserted into the lumen of the next pipe. In view of the quantity of water needed, many of these tree trunks were laid alongside each other along the streets. Maitland records that "This stream is ingulphed at Islington by 58 main pipes, of seven inches bore, which convey it in others through the streets of London, and its suburbs, into upwards of 30,000 houses, in leaden pipes of one inch bore". (8). It is reported that boys discovered that by drilling a hole in the pipes a magnificent fountain could be created and New River Company officials had to patrol them to tend to leakages. Water was delivered to the ground floor of houses through lead pipes and swan-necked cocks "so that by this simple contrivance it is perfectly easy to regulate the current with the greatest exactness." (9).

In order to avoid any conflict with Peter Morris's London Bridge Waterworks Company, the New River Company did not lay any pipes in that part of the City

7

immediately to the north of London Bridge, a decision which was to prove disastrous about fifty years later when the Fire of London started in that area. (see page 18).

After the opening ceremony the king conferred a knighthood on Sir Hugh Myddelton; in October 1622 he was created a baronet. Sir Hugh died on 10 December, 1631. Following application to James I, the Charter of the New River Company was granted on 21 June, 1618. The seal depicted "the hand of Providence issuing from the clouds and throwing down rain upon the City of London" with the motto: Et plui super unam Civitatem — and I caused it to rain upon one city (Amos ch. 4 v. 7). The seal showed St. Pauls Cathedral; this was, of course, the old St. Pauls which was destroyed in the fire of London in 1666.

The number of customers rose slowly. By the end of the first year of operation the Company was supplying 175 houses and one year later it had increased to 384; it was not until the fifth anniversary that the number topped 1,000 (28). However we are told that in 1809 the New River supplied 59,058 houses (2) with an average of 196 gallons a day each and that in 1834 73,212 houses were supplied, and that the average daily supply to each house was 241 gallons (26). As the elm pipes were of narrow bore, and could not retain water under pressure, large numbers were needed lying together to carry the supply. The pipes were bored with long iron augers which were rotated and the elm tree trunks were pushed against them. Two methods of rotating the augers were used. They were attached to a water wheel where flowing water was available, or ropes were wound round the shafts and attached to horses which would walk in opposite directions, unwinding the ropes as they did so.

Elm tree trunks were used for pipes for 200 years from 1613. A section of pipe was used as an umbrella stand in the New River Company offices

Sections were also used as clock cases

## 4.   Financing the Undertaking

The cost of building the New River has been the subject of calculation and conjecture as the early records of the Company were destroyed by fire in 1769. Kent states categorically that it cost £500,000 (7) whereas Samuel Smiles in his 'Lives of the Engineers' in 1861 put it at £17,000.   However when the King became involved Myddelton had to submit detailed accounts to the Lord High Treasurer. These are preserved in the Public Record Office and show that from 20 February, 1608, until 26 November, 1614 (by which time water mains had been laid to the City), the total expenditure amounted to £18,527.0.1d (33).

As mentioned, Hugh Myddelton offered to pay for the scheme himself, but after about a year his money became depleted and his request to the Corporation of London for funds was of no avail.   Eventually, in 1612, King James I offered to provide half the cost of the entire project in return for half the profits and properties being ceded to His Majesty.   To facilitate this, the concern was divided into seventy-two equal parts, thirty-six being retained by the Company – the "Adventurers' Moiety" – and the remainder were given to the King – the "King's Moiety".

When the New River Company was incorporated in 1619 management was vested in the twenty-nine Adventurers (who owned the thirty-six shares between them).   The investment proved to be an unprofitable speculation at first as after nineteen years each of the seventy-two shares yielded a profit of about twelve shillings (2).   When Charles I became King following his father's death in 1625, he negotiated with Sir Hugh Myddelton to be relieved on his moiety of 36 shares in return for a perpetual annuity of £500, known as the King's Clog, from 1630.

The 36 King's Shares and the 36 Adventurers' Shares were each real estate and could be passed by deed of conveyance like freehold property.   These shares could be sub-divided but some have remained intact; at an auction held on Wednesday 21 May, 1890 for "A King's Freehold Share (being a one 72nd part of the entire concern) in this Grand Historic Corporation" the share was sold at £95,100 (30).

9

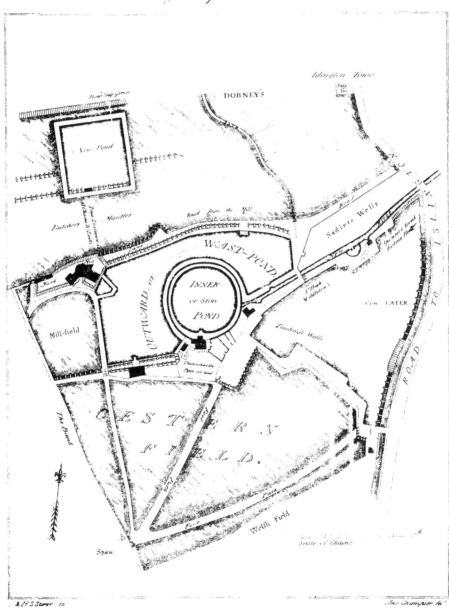

An Actual SURVEY of the New River Head near Islington 1753

10

## 5.   Alterations to the New River and its water supply (Map 2)

The earliest alteration to the course of the channel was at Highbury where, in September 1619, a 462ft timber aqueduct seventeen feet high diverted the New River over Hackney Brook; similar to the Bush Hill Frame, it was known locally as 'the boarded river'. The long loop which ran as far as Holloway Road was therefore abandoned only six years after it had been constructed.

Myddelton could be forgiven for thinking that the springs at Chadwell and Amwell would supply London with sufficient fresh water for a considerable period. However, within fifty years the flow was inadequate and an Act of 1660 authorised the New River Company to extract water from the River Lee. This raised much protest from mill owners who relied on the Lee to drive their water wheels and from bargemen who used the navigation for supplying grain and malt to the City. The trouble persisted for years and numerous court cases resulted from disputes. In a judgement on 5 May, 1666 "Mr. Dunstan is commanded at his peril not to cut any of the banks of the New River" and on 7 July, 1668 a bargeman petitioned the City for some compensation" . . . for his charge and pains for removing a great obstruction and hindrance caused by the governors of the New River to the common passage and navigation in and upon the river Lee." Over a year later, on 22 September, 1669, a court decided "The governor and company of the New River do take away their great pipes now lying in the river Lee and instead do lay two lesser pipes." (10). An Act of Parliament in 1738 attempted to settle the disputes and the amount of water extracted was limited to twenty-two and a half million gallons a day. A timber gauge was built in the New River to measure the flow and this was replaced in 1770 by a marble gauge – which is still present though not now in use. A wooden balance engine spanned the channel; it consisted of a sluice gate at one end of a large oak beam and a boat at the other so arranged that changes in the level of the Lee would raise or lower the sluice to maintain a constant flow of water into the New River. This was replaced in 1856 by the New Gauge in which the floats are iron pontoons; 22½ million gallons a day is the maximum flow which will enter the New River, but the flow can be reduced by hanging metal plates on the weir to restrict its width – these plates ae called "million-gallon-a-day plates" and they are still in use. (see page 29). The "Balance House" stood just behind the "Gauge House" but it was removed in 1926 and no remnant is present today.

In 1709 an Upper Pond was built in Claremont Square some two hundred yards further up the hill above the round pond at New River Head to provide a greater head of water so that more houses could be supplied. Initially water was pumped to it from the round pond by a windmill but this was replaced in 1720 by a 'horse mill'.

View of London
1752 from Islington Bowling
Green. (see map opposite)

Writing about the City of London in his "Tour through the Whole Island of Great Britain" in 1724, Daniel Defoe describes this pump soon after the sails were replaced by horses: "The New-River, which is brought by an aqueduct or artificial stream from Ware, continues to supply the greater part of the city with water, only with this addition by the way, that they have been obliged to dig a new head or basin at Islington on a higher ground than that which the natural stream of the river supplies, and this higher basin they fill from the lower, by a great engine worked formerly with six sails, now by many horses constantly working; so from that new elevation of the water, they supply the higher part of the town with the same advantage, and more ease, than the Thames engines do it" (31).

Sir Christopher Wren (the son of the architect of St. Pauls) was consulted in 1753 about a scheme for providing a further pump at the round pond to supply water "to Soho and the higher parts of the neighbourhood, to which it comes but weakly". The engine, to be worked by three horses, was estimated to deliver 60 tuns of water an hour and would cost £300, the horses costing a further £150 a year. Wren challenged the costs and concluded "Upon the whole matter, I think an engine is not adviseable, if the place can be supplied without one, as I think it may." (11).

In 1766 John Smeaton was consulted about the horse-engine pumping water to the upper pond in Claremont Square and reported "4 horses in March 1766 raised, at the rate of 7 strokes a minute which it then made with each forcier, that it raises (or ought to raise) at the rate of 42 tuns of water an hour, but if two tuns is allowed for leakage and waste, we may bona fide reckon upon 40 tuns an hour, and as the engine is kept going 16 hours out of 24, there will be raised at least 640 tuns a day." He then discussed the effect of increasing the horses to six and to eight but the following year a small Newcomen steam engine was installed in place of the horse-engine (12). About twenty years later this gave way to a Boulton and Watt engine, and electric pumps were introduced in 1950.

At Bush Hill the lead trough in the 'Frame' over Salmons Brook was raised one foot higher in 1725 and the frame was replaced entirely by a clay bank in 1786, some ten years after a similar embankment was built to replace the frame in Highbury. (see page 20).

The earliest record of a surveyor or engineer to the New River Company was Henry Mill (1720-1771). Robert Mylne was appointed as his assistant in 1767 and succeeded him in 1771. In 1775 Mylne replaced the Myddelton timber 'flash' carrying Cuffley Brook over the New River near Crews Hill with one of stone — remnants of which can be seen today — and in 1793 he began laying cast-iron pipes; "these wonderful and magnificent pipes are bedded in the earth below the original wooden ones and supported at intervals in the notches of a stout wooden post or stake burnt at the end." (13). His son, William Chadwell Mylne was appointed assistant engineer in 1804 and followed his father as Chief Engineer in 1811, a post he held for fifty years. In 1810 he reported to the Company that there were some 400 miles of wooden pipes in London and that these would have to be replaced with cast iron pipes during the next ten years. In 1820 he shortened the loop in Whitewebbs Park by half a mile by building a cast-iron aqueduct over Cuffley Brook. The aqueduct, which has been excavated recently, cost £252.2.0d (6) and is similar in design to Telford's aqueduct at Longton-on-Tern on the Shrewsbury Canal (1795) and the Pontcysyllte on the Llangollen Canal (1805). The loop was finally abandoned in 1859 when Docwra built an aqueduct over Maidens Brook and a one mile embankment. However the old course from Crews Hill was used again forty years later as a feeder from a pumping station built in 1898.

Further straightening of the course of the New River has been taking place in the past one hundred and forty years. In 1852 the detour out towards Tottenham was obviated by a seven hundred yard brick tunnel, fourteen feet in diameter, at Wood Green and a two hundred yard, seven foot diameter tunnel was built through the hill under Wightman Road, Harringay. The Turnford aqueduct was built by William Chadwell Mylne in 1855 to eliminate the loops near Broxbourne and the loop in Arnos Park was by-passed by an aqueduct over Pymmes Brook. The loop around Enfield Town was made redundant when underground pipes were installed between Enfield Town and Bush Hill; the pipes were bombed in October 1940, so the old course was reinstated. It was handed back to the Council in November, 1952 and the water authority agreed to maintain a small water supply to the loop to retain its amenity. From time to time the New River was widened and its banks raised in order to increase its capacity. To regulate the flow of water sluice gates, consisting of wooden shutters which could be raised or lowered by a rack and wheel, were placed at Amwell Hill, Broxbourne, Cheshunt, Whitewebbs, Enfield, Bush Hill, Hornsey and Highbury. These were later replaced by roller sluices.

In 1830 William Chadwell Mylne began the construction of reservoirs, the first two being at Stoke Newington in 1831 and 1833; the western reservoir is lined with stones taken from the old London Bridge which was being demolished. Reservoirs in Cheshunt were completed in 1837. The cholera epidemic of 1846 led to the setting up of a Select Committee to consider the purity of domestic water; bathing in the New River – a popular pastime – was stopped and in compensation the Company offered to supply free water to public baths. The Metropolis Water Act, 1852, required water companies to filter all domestic water and to store it in covered reservoirs so Mylne constructed filtration works at Stoke Newington, Hornsey and New River Head, Islington.

The demand for water continued to increase so the Company began sinking wells with steam pumps along the course of the New River. The dates and depths of the twelve wells were: Amwell Hill 1847 (160 feet), Turnford 1850 (1,010 ft), Hoddesdon 1866 (385 ft), Amwell End 1868 (419 ft), Broadmead 1880 (500 ft), Hoe Lane 1880 (395 ft), Rye Common 1883 (204 ft), Amwell Marsh 1884 (392 ft), Highfield 1885 (371 ft), Broxbourne 1886 (212 ft), Campsbourne 1887 (396 ft) and Whitewebbs 1898 (402 ft). A typical well consists of a circular shaft 12-15 feet in diameter, lined with cast iron or brickwork, through the upper strata and continued down through the clay until chalk is reached. From here galleries 6 feet high and 4 feet wide are driven sideways, sometimes for considerable distances, to cut water channels in the chalk. Perhaps the most extraordinary pumping station built by Mylne was that at Stoke Newington in 1855 to pump water from reservoirs. It is said that the site was adjacent to a noble estate and in order to preserve its grandeur the pumphouse was built to resemble a castle. The steam engines in all the pumping stations were replaced by electric pumps between 1935 and 1955.

The southernmost section of the New River from Colebrooke Row to New River Head was piped in 1861 and that from Stoke Newington to Douglas Road by 1870, leaving a small stretch of open water between St. Pauls Road and Canonbury Road. The use of the Round Pond at New River Head ceased in 1914 and the surrounding filter beds were abandoned in 1945. The New River was then terminated at Stoke Newington and the pipes from there to Islington were re-used for the Lee Valley reservoirs.

The New River has been widened over the years to accommodate the increased water flow from the wells; where this has been difficult, for instance under bridges, an 'easement channel' has been built around the constriction. Tunnels, usually iron pipes some 48 in. or more in diameter, accept surplus water upstream of the bridge, carry it under the adjoining land in a sweep to by-pass the narrowing and then return it to the main river beyond the bridge. Examples may be seen at the road bridge near Ware Station, at the approach to the lakes at Great Amwell and where the New River passes beneath the twin bridges at Fords Grove and Farm Road, Winchmore Hill.

The New River Company sought to increase its supply of water from other sources and acquired the resources and distribution system of other water companies such as the York Buildings Water Works Company in 1818, the London Bridge Water Works in 1822 and the Hampstead Water Company in 1859; water from the latter was used for non-domestic purposes only (27). Its water responsibilities were purchased by the Metropolitan Water Board for £6,534,000 in 1904 (7) and acquired by Thames Water Authority in 1974. The New River Company Ltd. still administers its other properties.

More recent changes to the New River have been necessitated by road developments. When the North Circular Road was improved at Bowes Road, Palmers Green, in 1963 the New River had to be diverted under the road in a 'U-bend' conduit; a special weed trap was installed to prevent blockage of the channel beneath the road. The A10(T) Ware By-pass was constructed on a high viaduct across the Lee Valley in the mid 1970s, not over the New River itself but over the feeder from the River Lee intake; the road provides an excellent high-level view of Chadwell Spring. And when, in the early 1980s, the M25 London Orbital Motorway was built between Waltham Abbey and Potters Bar, account had to be taken of the New River which crossed its route close to the A10 Cambridge Road. The need to maintain the water channel, established at the beginning of the 17th century, was one of the factors which influenced the decision to lower the Motorway into a cutting so that a concrete aqueduct could be constructed to carry the water over the traffic.

Weeds growing in the water are cut by specially shaped scythes on a chain; these are drawn to and fro in the river by a man on either bank walking upstream so that the current bends the trailing weeds towards the blades. The weeds float down the stream and are removed by staff with rakes at various collecting points. In 1984 an automatic weed remover was installed at the entrance to the aqueduct over Maidens Brook at a cost of £55,000 (see page 40).

6.   The New River Today

The present length of the New River from Hertford to Stoke Newington is approximately twenty miles. Chadwell Spring, the River Lee intake and the pumping stations along its course supply thirty-eight million gallons of fresh water daily; eight million gallons are at present abstracted at Hornsey and Campsbourne Pumping Station and the rest at Stoke Newington. In Hertfordshire a public walk is maintained alongside the New River throughout most of its length, but in the London Boroughs of Enfield, Haringey and Hackney there is very little easy access to it.

Thames Water Authority is undertaking a comprehensive scheme to reorganise London's water distribution.   This includes building a ring main – a tunnel eight feet in diameter – encircling London and the modernisation and uprating of London's water treatment works, due for completion in 1994.

At present water flowing in the New River is treated at Stoke Newington and Hornsey works and then distributed to East London.   Part of the scheme is to discontinue the use of these treatment plants and the Stoke Newington reservoirs. Originally it was planned to build a new treatment works at Cheshunt, making the New River south of Cheshunt redundant for the needs of Thames Water Authority in providing domestic water for London.   However a survey at the Cheshunt site revealed difficulties and in view of an increased demand for water in East London – particularly in relation to the Docklands Development Scheme – the decision now is to increase the Coppermills Treatment Plant in Walthamstow instead and to divert the New River water to the King George V Reservoir in a tunnel under the A10 and the River Lee.   The New River will therefore continue to be needed as far as the new automatic weed remover (see page 40), just beyond Turkey Street.

Building the new tunnel to divert the New River to East London

15

In the past most stretches of the New River no longer required by the water authority have been de-watered; notable exceptions to this are the Horseshoe loop around Enfield, the lake in Clissold Park and the length alongside New River Walk in Canonbury, which are maintained by the local authorities as an amenity. Thames Water Authority diverts a small flow of water from the New River into the loop round Enfield. Of the rest, some remain as ditches which may contain water — especially in wet weather — such as between Theobalds Park and the M25 Motorway, in Whitewebbs Park and in Arnos Park. Other lengths have been built over, for instance between Clay Hill, Enfield, and Tenniswood Road, between Green Lanes, Southgate and Arnos Park, the entire Edmonton loop, in Hornsey and in Harringay, and on the site of the Highbury Frame or 'Boarded River' west of Stoke Newington. The most recent building constructed over the old course is the Dame Alice Owen Building near Sadlers Wells. These are described in detail in later pages.

However Thames Water Authority has initiated discussions with the local authorities concerned and several conservation groups and local history societies are considering the possible consequences of a further section of the present course being abandoned. Suggestions have included the use of the old course as a linear park or footpath and the preservation of the water channel as an amenity and for wildlife. Following meetings with the New River Action Group, a body representing several organisations along the course of the New River campaigning to conserve the amenity, Thames Water has offered to continue to supply water to the redundant channel as it does in Enfield. However although 0.1 million gallons a day is fed into the horseshoe loop, leakage from the channel in Enfield Park makes this flow inadequate and the Authority's proposed 13 million gallons a day to the section of the New River it no longer needs — one third of the present volume — is a substantial improvement. The filter beds at Hornsey, below Alexandra Palace, have been suggested as an extension to the nature reserve beside them. The Stoke Newington filter beds and reservoirs were the subject of a Thames Water Authority exhibition of options for their use when they are no longer needed; the public response on questionnaires provided at the time were analysed. One proposal is that the west reservoir will be developed as a conservation area and that building will be allowed on the filter beds and east reservoir. Consultation with local authorities is proceeding.

The New River and its pumping stations between Hertford and Maidens Brook in Enfield, and the intake from the River Lee, continue to feature in the future plans of the Thames Water Authority.

# CONTEMPORARY REFERENCES TO THE NEW RIVER

*In plays written 1601-1639*

Discussions on the need for a supply of fresh water for London and on how this might be obtained and the construction of the New River all took place while Shakespeare was writing and presenting his plays in London between 1590 and 1612. Shakespeare often made allusions to matters of interest to his audiences in his plays but, surprisingly, no reference to the problems of a domestic water supply has been found.    However several other dramatists of the time did mention London's water and the New River.    Ben Johnson, in his play "Every Man in his Humour" (1601) included a character Oliver Cob, a water bearer, who told his wife "I deal with water and not with wine.    Gi' me my tankerd there, ho.    It's six o'clock: I should ha' carried two turns by this.    What ho my stopple come." (See p.1).    Thomas Middleton (unrelated to Hugh or his brother, Sir Thomas Myddelton) wrote a pageant for the opening ceremony of the New River (1613):    "Triumphs of Truth.    A Solemnity unparaleled for Cost, Art, and Magnificence at the Confirmation and Establishment of that Worthy and true Nobly-minded Gentleman, Sir Thomas Middleton. . .   Showing also his Lordships Entertainment upon Michaelmas day last, being the day of his Election, at the most Famous and Admired Worke of the Running Streame, from Amwell-head into the Cesterne at Islington, being the sole Cost, Industry, and Invention of the Worthy Mr. Hugh Middleton of London, Goldsmith."    The Lord Mayor watched the performance from a mount alongside the round pond at Islington and saw "A Troope of Labourers, to the number of three-score or upwards, all in greene Cappes alike, bearing in their hands the Symboles of their severall imployments in so great a businesse with Drummes before them, marching twice or thrice about the Cesterne, orderly present themselves before the Mount;".

Beaumont and Fletcher in their play "Wit at Several Weapons" (1613) – Act 4, had Pompey Doodle, the Clown, say:   ". . . if you chance to meet a footman by the way. . . direct him and his horses toward the new River by Islington, there shall they have me, looking upon the Pipes, and Whistling." and then (Act 5) "Clown:  I was ne'er so cold in my life, in my conscience I have been 7 mile in length along the New River: I have seen a hundred sticklebacks".    Later in the same scene "Well, I will go walk by the New River. . . . if she sends I shall be found angling, for I will try what I can catch."    In their play "Wit Without Money – A Comedie, as it hath been Presented with good Applause at the private house in Drurie Lane by her majesties servants, 1639" Valentine declares "Stirre not, but heare, and marke, Ile cut your throats else, till Waterworkes, and rumours of new Rivers rid you again and runne you into questions who built the Thames. . ."

Henry Glapthorne, in "Hollander" (1635) portrayed a drinking scene in Act 4 with the dialogue:
"Fortress:  Thou shalt be my Bacchus Io, he drinkes as if hee had eaten Pickle Herring.
Sconce:  This Cup was as deepe as Fleet-street Conduit.  Sound me my Io, I ha' made a new River in my Belly, and my Guts are the Pipes".

17

*Contract for a supply of domestic water – 1616*

A householder seeking a supply of water from the New River Company had to sign a lengthy contract with Hugh Myddelton. For twenty-six shillings and eight pence per annum, Myddelton:

". . . hath demised and granted, &c. a quill or branch of lead containing halfe an inch of water or thereabouts the said branch to be taken from the main pipe that lyeth in ⸻ Streete and from thence to be convaied in the foresaid pipe of lead by tooe of the smallest swan-necked cockes for that purpose already imployed into the yarde and kitchnie of the now dwelling house of ⸻ and ⸻ his wife . . . if they or either of them shal so long dwell in the said house wherein now they do and use no other trade than now they do for greater expenses of water." (9)

*The Fire of London – 1666*

Certainly in the sixteenth century Londoners appreciated the risk of fire in the City because one argument in support of the granting of a lease in 1582 to Peter Morris for his pump at London Bridge was "for the better service of the City in case of casualty by fire" (3). (see page 2). In the City Records dated 13 November, 1623, the benefits of having water from the New River running in pipes along the streets is noted "especially att many great fires happened within this Citty, and Chefely the last night at a verie terrible and fearefull fire which might greatly have endangered the Cittye, had that needefull water binn wanting" (28). The water was obtained by cutting the pipes and flooding the street, but in 1634 the Common Council arranged for cocks to be provided in the mains for use for fire-fighting.

The New River featured in a number of accounts of the Fire of London which broke out in Pudding Lane, near London Bridge at about one-thirty in the morning of Sunday 2 September, 1666. Myddelton had decided not to supply New River water to the area served by the London Bridge Waterworks Company in order to avoid any conflict with that company (see page 7). Two reports, describing the spread of the fire, highlight the consequences of this decision.

"Before long Fishmongers' Hall was alight, the first of the forty-four Halls of the City Companies to perish. The water house by the Bridge connected with Morice's waterwheels beneath the northern arches soon followed, so that the water system with its pumps could no longer be used to stay the fire. . ." (14)

"The fire spreading four ways at once, it reached an inn full of hay, etc; another branch extended to Thames Street. . . and the two branches meeting at London Bridge destroyed it, with all the waterworks, so that the New River water not being laid into those parts, no water could be had to oppose its fury." (15)

The cause of the fire, we read, was "reciprocally charged by the Papists and fanatics upon one another" (15) and a Westminster schoolboy called Taswell recalled "the ignorant and deluded mob. . . vented forth their rage against the Roman Catholics and Frenchmen; imagining these incendiaries (as they thought) had thrown red-hot balls into the houses." (14). This could account for the following story in the Gentleman's Magazine related by Bishop Burnet of Salisbury:

"One Grant, a Papist. . . acquired a right to view the (New River Company)

18

works whenever he pleased. 'It is affirmed,' says the Bishop, 'by the officer of the works that having set the cocks running on that Saturday on which the fire happened, this Grant came and, demanding the keys, turned all the cocks and stopped the water, carrying the keys away with him, so that when the fire broke out no water could be had till a messenger had been dispatched to Islington, and turned on the water'." (15)

The report in the Gentleman's Magazine adds that the New River Company Minute Book reveals that Grant was not a member of the Company until after the date of the fire.

Daniel Defoe, in his 'Tour through the Whole Island of Great Britain' – 1724 – writes:

"No where in the world is so good care taken to quench fires as in London; I will not say the like care is taken to prevent them for I must say that I think the servants, nay, the masters too in London, are the most careless people in the world about fire . . ."

"And this leads me back to what I just now said, that no City in the world is so well furnished for the extinguishing fires when they happen.
1. By the great convenience of water which being everywhere laid in the streets in large timber pipes, as well from the Thames as the New-River, those pipes are furnished with a fire plug, which the parish officers have the key of, and when opened, let out not a pipe, but a river of water into the streets, so that making a dam in the kennel, the whole street is immediately under water to supply the engines.
2. By the great number of admirable engines . . . so that no sooner does a fire break out, but the house is surrounded with engines, and a flood of water poured upon it, 'till the fire is, as it were, not extinguished only, but drowned.
3. The several insurance offices have each of them a certain set of men, who they keep in constant pay. . . These they call fire-men, but with an odd kind of contradiction in the title, for they are really most of them water-men" (31).

*Percy Histories, 1824*

"The main pipes of the New River company were originally of wood but they are now almost entirely of cast iron. A large bason has been constructed in the Hampstead-road, which receives its water from Islington, in order to supply the western parts of the town. The number of houses supplied by the New River is up-wards of fifty-six thousand, which is continually increasing, particularly since the water-works have been recently taken down at London-Bridge." (2)

*C F Partington, 1835*

"The contrivances for the distribution of the water through the several parts of London, are admirable. From a circular bason which first receives it, the water is conveyed by sluices into several brick cisterns; whence it passes through large wooden pipes* of six or seven inches diameter, called mains and riders, to the various districts of the capital, into the houses of which it is carried by means of leaden pipes, under which all the water passes; so that by this simple contrivance it is perfectly easy to regulate the current with the greatest exactness.

*The company have also introduced large pipes of iron for this purpose." (9)

19

In September 1784 a correspondent's description of the Bush Hill Frame was published in the Gentleman's Magazine:

"The annexed plate" (Plate 1) "exhibits a view of the wooden aqueduct near Bush Hill, in the Parish of Edmonton, made 1608 for the conveyance of the New River, where the natural level of the ground was unfavourable. This being the only one now remaining (for a similar aqueduct at Highbury, near Islington, was taken away and replaced by a bed of clay, about six years ago); I thought a representation of it would not be disagreeable to your readers, especially as preparations for removing this also are now actually going forward under the direction of Mr. Mylne, Surveyor to the New River Company. The length of this wooden trough is 660 feet; its height and depth five." It adds: "The house seen at the right corner is the Green Dragon public house, where penny-post letters are received." (16a)

In the following month an engraving of the Clarendon Arch beneath the Bush Hill Frame appeared (Plate 2). "Over the point of the arch are the arms of Sir Hugh Middleton: On a pile of 3 wolves heads counter-changed; Crest, a hand displayed issuing out of a coronet" (16b). This was an attempt at: 'Argent on a pile vert three wolves' heads couped of the field. Crest, a hand displayed issuing out of a coronet'. (Burke's Armory, 1884).

These entries encouraged a further correspondent to write to the Magazine about the Highbury Aqueduct; it was published in November, 1784.

"The Boarded River, as it used generally to be called, about half-way between Highbury, in the Parish of Islington, and Hornsey Wood House, in the Parish of Hornsey, was about 178 yards long. It was carried over an ancient bridle-way; and as I used frequently to pass under it in the summer-time, I observed it to be almost continually dropping. This being literally such a constant drain upon the Company, first, I suppose, suggested the idea of destroying it. Accordingly, about midsummer, 1776, preparations were made for that purpose. The earth was raised, by the addition of a great bed of clay, to a proper level, and a channel was made for the river nearly along the old track." (16c)

And in May, 1788, we read in the same magazine:

"In the course of this month, the frame or trough in which the New River run near Bush-hill Edmonton as described in our Vol. LIV pp 643 773* was completely removed, the water having continued near 12 months in its new bed of earth and clay. The old lead, amounting to near 50 tons, was sold at 18s per ton to five plumbers." (16d). (*This was a misprint for p 723; quotations (16a) and (16b) above refer).

The Highbury embankment seemed to cause a number of problems. On Friday 13 April, 1787:

"About 5 o'clock in the afternoon an accident happened at the New River ... When the frame, in which the river used formerly to be carried between Hornsey

Plate 1. Bush Hill Frame

Plate 2. Clarendon Arch, Bush Hill

Wood and Highbury, was removed in 1766 and a bed of clay substituted in its place, it was found necessary to carry a brick arch under the River, to preserve the course of a little stream, the parent of Hackney Brook; the crown of this arch gave way, and fell in immediately under the river." (16e)

And, on Sunday 2 September, 1798:

"This afternoon, about six o'clock, the North East bank of the New River suddenly burst, about half a mile from Hornsey House." (16f)

## Charles Lamb – Essays and Letters, 1775-1834

Charles Lamb spent much of his life near the New River and constantly mentioned it in his writings. While he was at school he was fired by Bruce's discovery of the source of the Nile and he set off with some friends "on one fine summer holyday (a "whole day's leave" we called it at Christ's hospital) sallying forth at rise of sun, not very well provisioned either for such an undertaking, to trace the current of the New River – Middletonian stream – to the scaturient source, as we had read, in the meadows by fair Amwell. Gallantly did we commence our solitary quest – for it was essential to the dignity of a DISCOVERY, that no eye of schoolboy, save our own, should beam on the detection. By flowery spots, and verdant lanes skirting Hornsey, Hope trained us on in many a baffling turn; endless, hopeless meadows, as it seemed; or as if the jealous waters had dodged us, reluctant to have the humble spot of their nativity revealed;" (17)

Charles Lamb lived with his sister alongside the New River in Islington from 1823 until 1827. In a letter dated 2 September, 1823, he wrote "I have a cottage in Colebrooke Row, Islington. . . The New River (rather elderly by this time) runs (if a moderate walking-pace can be so termed) close to the foot of the house;" (18) and Lucas in 1913 recommended a visit to "Colebrooke Row, at the end of which, in the last house on the north side, adjoining Duncan Terrace and next a ginger-beer factory, Charles Lamb once lived, in the days before the New River was covered over; and it was down Lamb's front garden that George Dyer walked when he fell into that stream." (19). Lamb recounts the incident in an essay written in December, 1823 "I do not know when I have experienced a stranger sensation than on seeing my old friend, G.D., who had been paying me a morning visit, a few Sundays back, at my cottage at Islington, upon taking leave, instead of turning down the right-hand path by which he had entered – with staff in hand, and at noonday, deliberately march right forwards into the midst of the stream that runs by us, and totally disappear." (20).

Charles Lamb and his sister visited Enfield in July 1825, staying with his friends, the Allsops, at their lodgings in Gentleman's Row beside the New River until September. They were there again for the summer of 1827 and on 10 August, 1827, he recorded in a letter "for I am. . . at Enfield Chase (Mrs. Leishman's). We have been here near three months". In September, he decided to settle in Enfield and sold his cottage in Colebrooke Row, writing in a further letter "The books, prints, &c. are come here, and the New River came down with us". The accommodation rented by Mrs. Leishman is Clarendon Cottage, number 17 Gentleman's Row.

*Charles Dickens: London Guide for 1879*

"New River. Was started in 1608 by Sir Hugh Myddelton. He was not Sir Hugh then, but a simple 'citizen and goldsmith', the baronetcy being a subsequent reward for the success of his great undertaking, which up to this day furnishes more than one-fourth the water supply of the metropolis. The New River is carried from the springs and chalk wells some twenty miles from London to the great reservoirs, 40 acres in extent, at Stoke Newington; thence, after time to clear itself, to the New River Head by Sadler's Wells Theatre – which in the old times had a special connection therewith, and could turn its stage into a huge tank for nautical exhibitions – and thence direct to the lower portions of the city or to the high-level reservoirs in Claremont Square and at Highgate." (21)

*Romance of the New River – Sir Alexander Houston, 1926*

"About 1804 an immense tank was constructed under and beyond the stage and was filled with New River water. On this aquatic stage a mimic representation of 'The Siege of Gibraltar' was given. It proved a gigantic success, attracting the nobility and even Royalty, as well as many thousands of lesser degree. Thomas Greenwood, scene painter at the Theatre, describes the successful venture as follows:-

'Attraction was needed, the town to engage,
So Dick emptied the River that year on the stage;
The House overflowed, and became quite the ton
And the Wells for some seasons, went swimmingly on' "

Sadlers Wells Theatre. c.1804

23

A note added "A fund has now happily been raised to save Sadler's Wells Theatre from becoming a mere memory of the past. The site has been purchased, the old walls still staunch and true, and soon a reconstructed theatre will carry on the old traditions." (22)

*History with a Sketchbook – Donald Maxwell, 1926*

"Sadler's Wells Theatre is now in course of reconstruction, to be, I believe, the Old Vic of North London. . . The stage of Sadler's Wells Theatre was built over the New River, and was used when uncovered for realistic aquatic effects. Whether the water of London occasionally tasted of orange peel and grease paint is not recorded." (23)

The Four Times of the Day: Evening
Print by William Hogarth, 25 March, 1739

An evening visit to Sadlers Wells by a pregnant lady who has cuckolded her husband walking beside her carrying the youngest child. The inn is the Sir Hugh Myddelton and in the foreground is the New River and a hollowed elm pipe. The smokers in the inn could refer to a tradition that Sir Hugh and Sir Walter Raleigh enjoyed smoking together (7); though it was probably Myddelton's brother who first smoked in public, Hogarth might well have represented the popular belief. Peter J. Naylor, who drew this picture to my attention, suggests that the glove carried by the lady is a reference to that on Myddelton's Crest and that the cow alludes to the people being milked for their water supply.

# EXPLORING THE NEW RIVER

Most of the New River is an open waterway which is easy to follow as it flows through fields and alongside roads, but at times it disappears behind fences, at the back of houses and through privately owned property. Similarly the old course may be traced through woods and public parks; it is more difficult to determine its precise course in some parts, though exciting clues may be discovered. I have consulted old maps (particularly the 6" Ordnance Survey maps prepared in 1779-1807) to locate the old course as nearly as possible and the 100ft contour is a reliable guide to either the original route or to the site of troughs and embankments built to avoid excessive detours.

The entire course — present and old — is described in sections of about three to four miles. Maps are added to supplement the text, but they are intended to serve only as a guide and are not strictly to scale. They should be used in conjunction with Ordnance Survey maps — sheets 166 and 176 (1:50,000 series) cover the entire course — and a London street atlas may be helpful. Suitable bus routes and railway stations are indicated for those wishing to explore the New River using public transport.

My descriptions of the present course and of the abandoned loops include sections which are not normally available to the public; permission was obtained from private owners and from the appropriate Authorities to visit and photograph these. Sometimes a view was obtained from a house-owner's garden but I have not identified the garden affording the best view because it could be unfair to the owner. Those exploring the New River should satisfy themselves that they are not trespassing while tracing its course; the fact that a section is included here does not necessarily signify free access to it.

In describing the present and the old course, I have usually used points of the compass to indicate the relationship of structures to one another. When I have referred to the right or left bank or right or left turns, I have assumed that the traveller is proceeding downstream.

*Hertford to Ware* (Map 3)

Chadwell spring, the original start of the New River, lies about 1½ miles east of Hertford, just to the east of the A10 Ware bypass which crosses the Lee Valley on a high viaduct. A panoramic view of the plain may be obtained from the viaduct, but a better view of the spring is from the A119 Hertford to Ware road just opposite the entrance to Chadwell Springs Golf Club. The spring itself is on property owned by Thames Water Authority. A public footpath, through an iron gate just to the left — that is towards Hertford — leads down to the plain where several structures, including the Marble Gauge, may be visited.

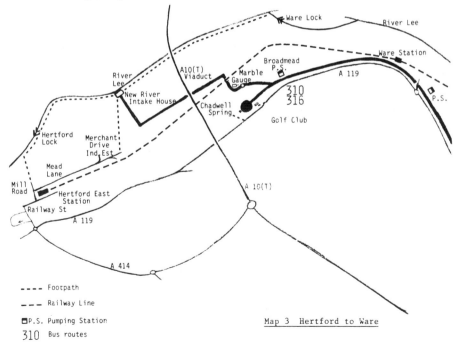

- - - - Footpath

— — — Railway Line

☐ P.S. Pumping Station

310 Bus routes

Map 3  Hertford to Ware

27

A picture postcard of Chadwell Spring, with the postmark 27 June, 1912

The spring rises in a circular basin 20 yards across and 18 feet deep and can yield up to 4 million gallons of water daily. In dry weather the flow can cease and a weir across the link with the New River, built during the great drought of 1898, prevents water running backwards into the dried-up spring. Opposite the outflow, on the west of the basin, stands a monument inscribed with dates and distances. On the four faces of the plinth we read "CHADWELL SPRING", "CONVEYED 40 MILES", "OPENED 1608" and "REPAIRD 1728", while on the east and west faces of the upper part of the monument is written "This Belongs to New River Company 178 Feet" and "This Belongs to the said Company 270 Feet" respectively. The north and south faces merely record "629 Feet" and "43 Feet". It has been suggested that the distances indicate the extent of the land opposite each face owned by the Company. Dotted about the land are several stone and iron markers bearing words like "This belongs to New River Company" or "NRCo". From the basin the New River flows eastwards where, in a short distance, it is joined by the feeder from the River Lee Intake.

The New River Intake from the River Lee, known also as the New Gauge, can be reached from Hertford East Station by going along Mill Road and turning right into Mead Lane which runs alongside the railway. Past the Merchant Drive Industrial Estate is a short, narrow lane which ends by a public footpath on the left. A wooden gate and a stile across the path lead directly to the brick building on the banks of the Lee Navigation. It may also be reached by walking along the towing path from Hertford or from Ware Lock. Ware Lock, incidentally, is owned by the Thames Water Authority because of the need to maintain the water level for the Intake House. The brick intake building stands by the side of the river and there is a grid through which water is taken in under the towing path. Inside there are two iron boats or pontoons connected by a curved cross-member which is linked to a weir plate 7ft. 10 inches in

28

width held constantly 16½ inches below the level of the River Lee. The water spilling over this weir plate drops into the feeder channel which emerges at the rear of the building. No more than 22½ million gallons a day may be extracted from the Lee; along the wall on the west side is a metal rail from which hang the 'one-million-gallon-a-day' plates and the 'half-million-gallon-a-day' plates; these can be hung from a bar over the weir plate to reduce its width − and hence the intake from the Lee − when required. Two scales indicate the levels of the water in the River Lee and in the New River. They consist of vertical strips, marked in centimetres, alongside which rise and fall pointers connected directly to floats, one on the Lee water and the other on the New River.

The first brick intake house was built in 1732 when Henry Mill was the Company's engineer and it was rebuilt in 1770 when Robert Mylne had been appointed to assist him. In a corner of the floor of the intake house at the time of my visit was an inscribed stone; it read:

REBUILT MDCCLXX
MILL AND MYLNE
ENGINEERS

The water enters the New River immediately behind the "Gauge House" − as it is called on old maps − and a short distance away the "Balance House" used to span the channel. This housed the old wooden balance engine (see page 11) which was replaced by the New Gauge in 1856 and we are told that this was being removed in 1926 (22); there is today no sign of its position as the channel was rebuilt in concrete some years ago. Dotted about the area are many iron 'NRC' markers delineating the boundary of the New River Company's property.

The feeder channel runs south towards the railway line and then turns eastwards to run under the new A10 viaduct. It turns south and east again crossing under the railway line, to a white, timber building, the 'white house sluice'. This is the first of nine sluices along the New River and here there is also a weir, built in 1746, to allow surplus water in the channel to be diverted into the River Lee. A short distance away is the 'Marble Gauge' beneath which the water had to flow through an opening 6ft. wide by 2ft. deep. This is no longer in use and is bypassed by two 24in. easement pipes, one on each side of it. Soon after this it joins the New River from Chadwell Spring and a short distance beyond the junction stands the first of the pumping stations and wells − Broadmead − which raises 0.4 million gallons a day (MGD). The New River then accompanies the road into Ware and swings southwards through Ware, still beside the road.

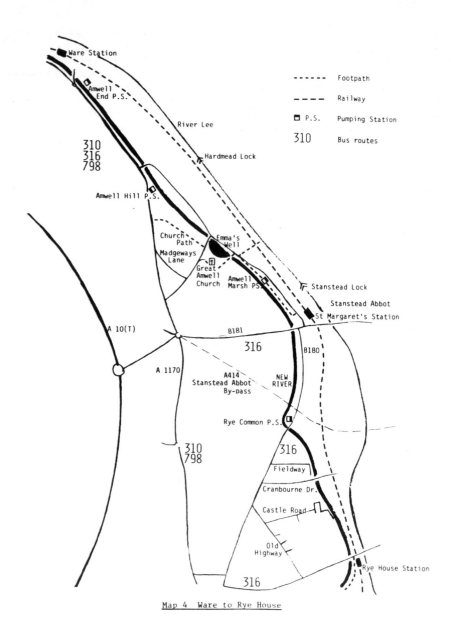

Map 4   Ware to Rye House

*Ware to Rye House* (Map 4)

As it leaves Ware, the New River passes Amwell End pumping station which also pumps 0.4 MGD.   About half a mile past Ware Station there is a turning on the left over a narrow bridge to Great Amwell.   The New River turns eastwards to run through fields where it passes Amwell Hill pumping station (0.5 MGD).   The entrance to the pumping station is on the main road and just past it pedestrians may take Church Path on the left to Great Amwell.   Motorists may take the next turn on the left – Madgeways Lane – and turn left at its end, bearing left down the hill to where the New River broadens into a small lake in which there are two attractive islands.   At the back Amwell Church is visible in the trees on the steep hillside and on the other side of the road the ground slopes down to the River Lee Navigation.

On the first island in the New River is a stone monument on which is inscribed part of a poem attributed to Archdeacon Nares in 1818.

> AMWELL.  Perpetual be thy Stream.
> Nor e'er thy Spring be less.
> Which thousands drink who never dream.
> Whence flows the boon they bless.
>
> Too often thus ungrateful man.
> Blind and unconscious lives.
> Enjoys kind Heav'ns indulgent plan.
> Nor thinks of Him who gives.

Maxwell claims that this is part of a poem entitled "Amwell" by John Scott, a Quaker poet and friend of Dr. Johnson, who lived in Amwell in the eighteenth century (24).   However it is more likely that the poem on the stone on the opposite side of the road (see below) is from Scott's "Amwell" as suggested by Houston (22).

On the second island is a memorial to Sir Hugh Myddelton, erected by Robert Mylne, engineer to the New River Company.   The inscription on the front (north) face is in latin while on the south, west and east faces respectively we read:

"Sacred to the memory of Sir Hugh Myddelton, Baronet, whose successful care assisted by the patronage of the King, conveyed this stream to London. An immortal work: Since men cannot more nearly imitate the Deity, than in bestowing Health."

"From the spring of Chadwell, two miles west and from this source of Amwell the aqueduct meanders for the space of 40 miles, conveying health, pleasure and convenience to the Metropolis of Great Britain."

"This humble tribute to the genius, talents and elevation of mind which conceived and executed this important aqueduct is dedicated by Robert Mylne, Architect, Engineer, &c. AD MDCCC".

On the opposite side of the road in a leafy hollow is 'Emma's Well'. An inscribed stone records:

"O'erhung with Shrubs that fringe the chalky rock
A little fount pours forth its girgling rill
In flinty channel bubbling o'er the green
From EMMA named perhaps some sainted maid
For holy life rever'd to such erewhile
Fond Superstition many a pleasant grove
And limpid Spring was wont to consecrate
Of Emmas Story nought tradition speaks
Conjecture, who behind Oblivions veil
Along the doubtfull past delights to stray
Boasts now indeed that from her well the place
Received its appellation.
In doomsday book this village of Amwell written Emmervelle"

This well is at a lower level than the New River and is almost certainly not the spring which formerly supplied it. "The Amwell spring has entirely disappeared, having oozed away silently about 1830 into the bed of the River Lee." (12)

Crossing the New River by the footbridge, climb up to the churchyard surrounding Amwell Church — the Parish Church of St. John Baptist, Great Amwell. Prominent there is a large family tomb capped by an inscription in latin which reads:

DEO OPT MAX
COEMETERIUM
PRO SE ET SUIS
DAT DON DEDICAT
ROBERTUS MYLNE
MDCCC

This is the tomb of the Mylne family in which are interred several generations between 1800 and 1920 and includes a servant who had been with W.C. Mylne for over fifty years. William Chadwell Mylne (April 1781 to December 1863) is buried there but not his father Robert (July 1733 to March 1811). A plaque on the tomb describes Robert as the designer of Blackfriars Bridge and "From the year 1767 he was engineer to the New River Aqueduct." He was buried, in accordance with his wishes, near the tomb of Sir Christopher Wren in St. Pauls Cathedral in London in 1811.

A short distance south of Amwell Church is Amwell Marsh pumping station, which raises 3.8 million gallons of water a day. As in all the present day pumphouses, the pumps are electrically operated.

There is a public footpath along the bank from Great Amwell to shortly before St. Margarets; although the embankment is much higher than the road, which accompanies it on its left-hand side, it will be noted that on the other side the channel was cut into the hillside. Just before the New River reaches the B181 Hertford to Stanstead Abbots road, it is necessary to descend the embankment on the footpath. There is an attractive view of the water, in both directions, from the bridge on the B181. Crossing under the road, the New River then continues beside the B180 — the road to Rye Park — to Rye Common pumping station (2.75 MGD) where the new A414 Stanstead Abbots by-pass crosses over. It then turns eastwards under the road and swings south to run alongside the end of Fieldway — a cul-de-sac off Stanstead Road on the left — and under the small bridge on Cranbourne Drive. From here the River Lee Navigation runs close to the New River — from which it is separated by the railway line — as far as Rye House Station. There is a well-worn path along the west bank from Cranbourne Drive, past playing fields and the end of Castle Road to Rye House but it is probably not a right of way. By road continue along the Stanstead road from Cranbourne Drive and turn left into Old Highway which leads to Rye House. Castle Road is a turning on the left off Old Highway and this affords a good view.

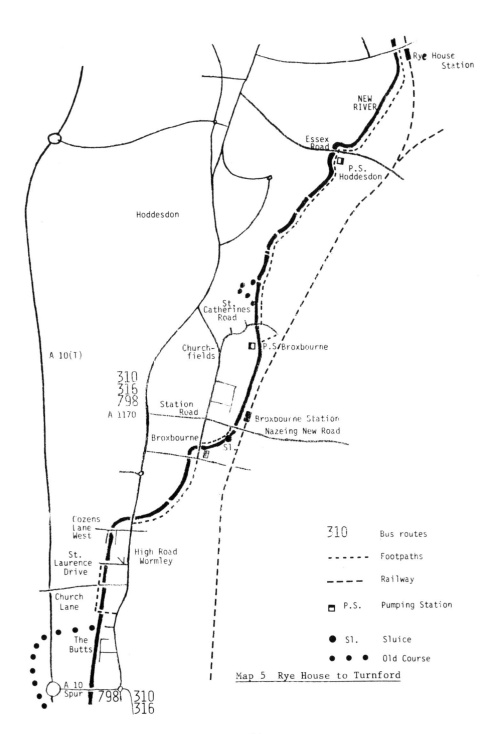

Rye House Station

NEW RIVER

Essex Road

P.S. Hoddesdon

Hoddesdon

St. Catherines Road

Church-fields

P.S. Broxbourne

A 10(T)

310
316
798
A 1170

Station Road

Broxbourne Station
Nazeing New Road

Broxbourne

Sl.

Cozens Lane West

St. Laurence Drive

High Road Wormley

Church Lane

The Butts

A 10 Spur

798

310
316

310      Bus routes

- - - - - -   Footpaths

- - - -   Railway

P.S.   Pumping Station

Sl.   Sluice

● ● ●   Old Course

Map 5   Rye House to Turnford

34

*Rye House to Turnford* (Map 5)

On the left of the bridge over the New River is a gate leading to a footpath between the River and Rye House railway station. A short distance along there is a fence which must be climbed; I am assured that this is a right of way – and is shown as such on the Ordnance Survey Map – but that a stile which used to be there has disappeared. On the left, near the fence, is an iron 'N.R.C.' marker such as may be seen at intervals along the course. The path ends in a gate to Essex Road and there is another gate between the New River and Hoddesdon Pumping Station (0.5 MGD) leading to a continuation of the footpath. This passes several footbridges, some of them grassy, and a 1967 bridge to Upper Marsh Lane. It is apparent along this length how the channel hugs the hillside adhering to the 100ft contour and the need for constant maintenance on the east bank to prevent leakage. The water is very clear and weeds growing on the clean bed can be seen trailing in the flowing stream. The path alongside the New River ends at a footbridge about 500 yards from Broxbourne. By walking down the path to the left, a stile on the right provided by a farmer gives access to a track across his field to the embankment of the New River; this provides a good view of Broxbourne pumping station (2.2 MGD) but there is no exit to Broxbourne. Return to the footbridge and cross it to St. Catherines Road – No. 47 is the entry to the pumping station – and thence into Churchfields which ends at Station Road. Turn left to the bridge.

Cross Nazeing New Road to the open space alongside which the New River runs, skirting Broxbourne Churchyard, a sluice-gate may be seen where it flows past the transformer station. It passes under an iron bridge dated 1868, another in front of the Church and a third – dated 1841 – before it swings south-west beside a footpath as far as Wormley where it crosses under the A1170.

On the west side of the A1170 it passes some attractive gardens and under a narrow iron bridge on Cozens Lane West to run behind the houses in St. Laurences Drive. Walk up this road bearing left, cross the footbridge near the school and walk beside the New River to Church Lane. Here, beside the hump-back bridge on its north eastern side, is a partly buried iron marker on which can be seen the letters N.R. , , – the 'C' is hidden. Continue on the footpath, turning left over the next bridge to emerge on Wormley High Road (opposite house number 131). Continue to the right down the main road; the cul-de-sacs on the right extend as far as the channel but it is seen best by turning right at the roundabout on the A10 spur. On the bridge over the New River look northwards; a line of trees extending westwards from the river, just where the embankment starts, marks the old course of the Wormley loop which swings round beyond the trunk road to return to the present course near Turnford pumping station. Cross the road and look southwards. Close by is the stone aqueduct over a small valley which was built to by-pass the loop. Turnford pumping station stands a short distance further downstream.

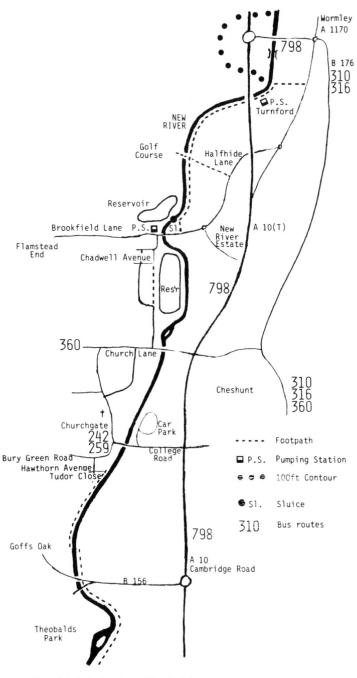

Map 6   Turnford to Theobalds

36

*Turnford to Theobalds* (Map 6)

Return to the roundabout south of Wormley Village and take the dual-carriage-way road marked "A10 London". A short distance along on the right – just past the lay-by (northbound carriageway) – take the "Public footpath: Brookfield Lane"; from here there is a good view of the Mylne aqueduct built in 1855. The New River is reached at a small slipway used for launching maintenance craft. Follow the path to the left towards Turnford pumping station. This is worth visiting (book in advance with TWA Waltham Cross) as it contains a preserved marine-type Boulton and Watt steam engine and a diesel engine as well as the electric pump now in use raising 0.8 MGD. The footpath follows the New River under the A10 and continues along its bank. Pass the footbridge leading to the golf course and go as far as the sluice in the stream. A stile on the left marks a footpath to Brookfield Lane. At the road turn right and cross the New River by the pumphouse which stands beside an open reservoir. This pump extracts treated water from the Cheshunt reservoir for the neighbourhood. On the south side of the road the River is diverted eastwards around the huge covered reservoir. Walkers should continue along Brookfield Lane and take the first turning on the left through the housing estate, behind the reservoir, to the next road which crosses the New River. If travelling down the A10, this point is reached by turning right at the first traffic lights, into Church Lane – sign-posted Flamstead End.

The steam pumping engine
preserved at Turnford
Pumping Station

Beyond here the New River swings westwards away from the A10 but it can be followed by turning left and going through the old part of Cheshunt, past the delightful church in Churchgate. At the bottom turn right into Bury Green Road, left into Hawthorn Avenue and left again into Tudor Close. Here a stile gives access to a footpath alongside the New River. Follow it southwards and cross a footbridge just before Theobalds Park. Motorists should bear left into College Road, cross the New River and turn right at the traffic lights. Continue south down the A10 to the roundabout and take the right exit marked B156. The New River crosses under this road before it circumvents Theobalds Park. This was once a royal estate and it is here that King James I went out riding with his son, Prince Charles, on a frosty winter's day on 9 January, 1622, when his horse stumbled and threw him into the ice-covered New River. He was rescued by Sir Richard Young "when there came much water out of his mouth and body" and survived the incident. In these grounds now stands Temple Bar awaiting a decision on whether it is to be restored to the City.

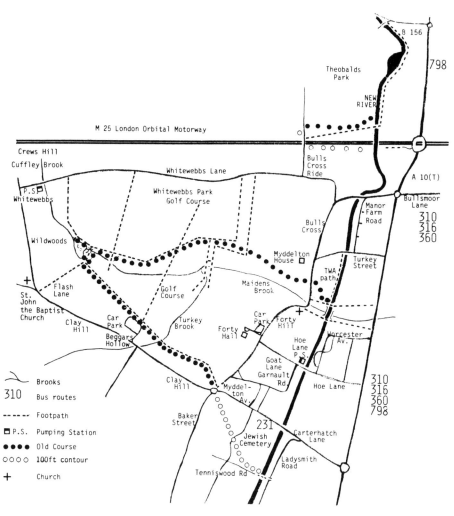

B 156

798

Theobalds
Park

NEW
RIVER

M 25 London Orbital Motorway

Crews Hill
Cuffley Brook

Whitewebbs Lane

Bulls
Cross
Ride

A 10(T)

P.S.
Whitewebbs

Whitewebbs Park
Golf Course

Manor
Farm
Road

Bullsmoor
Lane

310
316
360

Bulls
Cross

Wildwoods

Myddelton
House

Turkey
Street

TWA
path

Maidens
Brook

Flash
Lane
St.
John
the Baptist
Church

Golf
Course

Clay
Hill

Car
Park

Turkey
Brook

Car
Park

Forty
Hill

Forty
Hall

Worcester
Av.

Beggars
Hollow

Hoe
Lane
P.S.

Goat
Lane

Garnault
Rd.

310
316
360
798

Brooks

310    Bus routes

Clay
Hill

Myddel-
ton
Av.

Hoe Lane

------  Footpath

Baker
Street

231

Carterhatch
Lane

□ P.S.  Pumping Station

Jewish
Cemetery

●●●●  Old Course

Ladysmith
Road

OOOO  100ft contour

Tenniswood Rd

+    Church

Map 7  Theobalds to Enfield

38

*Theobalds to Enfield* (Map 7)

From the wooden footbridge over the New River on the south side of the B156, the footpath on the left continues round the east bank of the New River. A few yards from the gate, in the undergrowth on the left, is an iron 'N.R.C.' marker. Walk along this pleasant stretch of water where Theobalds House can be glimpsed through the trees, particularly where the channel widens with an island in the centre. Continue to the iron footbridge on the right. Ahead can be seen the new aqueduct carrying the channel over the M25 London Orbital Motorway and the way the carriage-way has been lowered below ground level is evident; the decision to put the motorway into a cutting – with a tunnel under Waltham Cross – was influenced by a number of factors, one of them certainly being the need to maintain the flow in this ancient water course.

Cross the footbridge to a narrow, sometimes overgrown footpath. Behind the fence on the right lies a deep ditch which holds water in wet weather – the old course of the New River which followed the 100ft contour as far as Bulls Cross Ride; the return loop has been obliterated by the Motorway. Walk down Bulls Cross Ride over the M25 and turn left onto Whitewebbs Lane. At the junction with Bulls Cross turn left to cross the present course. For a good view of the M25 aqueduct, go to the A10 roundabout over the M25 and take the track on the south side of the west-bound slip road.

From the bridge in Bullsmoor Lane, walk down Manor Farm Road; the New River courses due south to a very attractive iron bridge carrying Turkey Street over it. On the right-hand side of the bridge a private lane owned by Thames Water Authority runs along the bank of the New River to a point where the old course turned right towards Myddelton House. Here Thames Water Authority installed, in 1984, an automatic weed remover. The river flows through a grid and a pair of sensors compare the levels of the water on either side of it. If the grid should become blocked by weed, the upstream level will rise and this triggers a mechanical rake which lifts the weed from the water and deposits it in a skip on the bank.

Automatic weed remover between Turkey Street and Maidens Brook.
The new tunnel is being built in the background

The weed remover can be seen from a public footpath which links Bulls Cross to the A10(T) Cambridge Road; walk down Bulls Cross past a house called "Garnault" and some cottages to the entrance to a footpath on the left. This has become overgrown recently and entry to it can be achieved by walking up the private road alongside it for a short distance. The path crosses the New River between the weed remover and the aqueduct over Maidens Brook. It is here that the New River is being diverted into a tunnel – an access shaft can be seen between the weed remover and the path. The tunnel crosses diagonally under the sports ground between the footpath and Maidens Brook, towards the A10 and crosses under the River Lee to the King George V reservoir; the ancient supply of water for London is now to be used partly to supply the new Docklands Development.

The present course of the New River crosses Maidens Brook in an aqueduct faced in corrugated iron. This was built by Thomas Docwra of Cheshunt in 1859 and is best seen by proceeding further down Bulls Cross over the road bridge and taking the footpath on the left alongside Maidens Brook towards the A10. In a short distance the path crosses the end of the aqueduct and the New River continues on the Docwra embankment for about a mile, past the Hoe Lane Pumping Station, crosses under Carterhatch Lane and then lies alongside Ladysmith Road as far as the foot-bridge at the end of Tenniswood Road. Proceed down Bulls Cross into Forty Hill and turn left into Goat Lane (motorists will be unable to drive in at this end as it is a one-way street). Hoe Lane Pumping Station is actually in Goat Lane on the left just before the bridge; it can draw up to 100,000 gallons a day from a well. Opposite it is Garnault Road; follow it through to Carterhatch Lane, turn left over the bridge and cross the road to Ladysmith Road (the road is closed to through traffic near the footbridge).

The old course is clearly recognisable as it turns west from just above the weed remover and runs round the perimeter of the sports field to enter the grounds of the nineteenth century italianate house named "Garnault" (Mr. Garnault was a Treasurer of the New River Company whose service to the Company was recognised by the presentation of a silver cup in 1775). The tops of brick arches can be seen on either side of the road in the walls of "Garnault" and "Myddelton House" flanking Bulls Cross and there is a hump in the road between them where the bridge crossed the New River. Myddelton House was built in 1818 by Henry Bowles, who had married Anne Garnault; a century later the gardens were developed by E.A. Bowles, a disting-uished horticulturalist whose rare collection of plants encouraged the University of London to purchase the house and grounds in 1950 for its School of Pharmacy. The house and part of the garden were sold in 1967 to the Lee Valley Regional Park Authority from whom permission to visit must be obtained – unless advantage is taken of 'open days' when the public is invited to view the gardens. The old course of the New River was filled in in 1960 but an iron bridge dated 1832 remains just inside the wall where the New River entered the grounds and there are other remnants of bridges along the old course to the south of the house; the channel becomes visible again beyond the fence in agricultrual land. I have been told that when the old course was filled, spoil from the building of the Victoria Line was used. I have not been able to confirm this but the dates are consistent; the soil was deposited in the grounds of Myddelton House in 1960 and the Victoria Line was completed and opened in 1969.

Most of the old course can be traced in Whitewebbs Park. Return northwards up Bulls Cross and turn west along Whitewebbs Lane to the entrance to the park by the second lay-by on the left. In this park there is a bridle-way which, for the most part, is separate from the footpath but runs alongside it; here the bridleway is on the right-hand side. Walk down the footpath to the brídge over the old course which still holds water, especially in wet weather. The path swings right to follow the course as far as a gate onto the bridle-way – this was locked when I last visited it – and continues to the bridge over Maidens Brook. Turn right just before the bridge and a footpath leads back onto the bridle-way. Turn right towards the locked gate where the track crosses the old course and pass through the open gate on the left leading onto the golf course. From here it is easy to follow the old course, first along a tree-lined ditch, then across the golf course where it has been partly filled in, to a shrubbery where an old weir can be seen across the channel. This section is over-grown but it emerges by a wide public path.

This path begins in Whitewebbs Lane at a large car-parking area; if starting from here, take the path by the pink cottage. The old course can be readily identified continuing westwards from the path and may be followed along its southern side. A short distance along, the foundations of a small brick building may be seen in the undergrowth on the opposite bank. The channel, part of it in water, continues to the north end of the 1820 cast-iron aqueduct. Cross the muddy lane – Flash Lane – by two stiles and continue along the old course westwards, just to the north of the lake; an iron marker bearing the letters "NRCo" may be discovered in the undergrowth on the north side of the old course, proof that this was indeed the old course of the New River and not a dried up stream. On reaching Cuffley Brook the remnants of Robert Mylne's stone trough may be seen in the water on private land. The trough was built in 1775 to replace Myddelton's timber 'flash' aqueduct which carried the brook over the New River. It is suggested that Myddelton devised it this way so that he could tap the brook by means of this 'flash' for additional water supplies if needed. The stream from the north used to carry the water from Whitewebbs Pumping Station; it may be followed part of the way but it leaves the park, entering private land before it reaches the Pumping Station.

The 1820 Cast Iron Aqueduct on the now abandoned loop by Flash Lane in Whitewebbs Park.

The loop beyond Flash Lane was by-passed in 1820 by a cast-iron aqueduct over Cuffley Brook; this was cast by Hunter and English of Bow, London, and cost £252.2.0d (6). It was excavated recently by the Enfield Archaeological Society and its structure can be readily appreciated. The iron trough is carried on three brick columns and brick parapets have been added on each side making an attractive bridge. When the diversion was accomplished, the redundant loop was purchased by Edward Harman, who was improving his estate, so that he could dam Cuffley Brook to form an ornamental lake which now forms part of Wildwoods Estate. The southern arm of the loop between the flash aqueduct and Flash Lane was thus obliterated.

In 1898 Whitewebbs pumping station was built near Crews Hill and the old channel on the north side of the brook was reopened and used as a feeder to the New River near Turkey Street; the water therefore flowed in the opposite direction to the way it ran when it was part of the New River. Whitewebbs pumping station ceased pumping about 1950 but it is worth visiting; it stands on the left of Whitewebbs Lane about two miles west of Bulls Cross. It has recently been acquired by the Enfield and District Veteran Vehicle Trust which is restoring it for use as a motor museum.

From the cast-iron aqueduct the course runs due south for about 150 yards and swings eastwards, running along a belt of shrubs and trees beside a footpath to the south of Whitewebbs Park. Alternative access to this section is from Clay Hill, either down Flash Lane opposite St. John's Church, or from Whitewebbs Golf Club (down Beggars Hollow). Near the car park is an elegant brick bridge carrying the roadway over the now filled-in New River. From here the course swings south-east, where it crossed Turkey Brook, and continues in the grounds of Forty Hall to end in a small lake at the corner of Clay Hill and Forty Hill; the section from Turkey Brook to Clay Hill is in water. From Clay Hill the old course has been built over but it must have re-entered the present course just south of the Jewish Cemetery near the end of Tenniswood Road, Enfield, where the ground level can be seen to rise to that of the New River on its embankment. The whole of this loop was abandoned in 1859 when Docwra carried the New River in a straight course over Maidens Brook.

A picture postcard of Enfield 1909. The New River loop in Whitewebbs was then being used as a feeder from Whitewebbs Pumping Station.

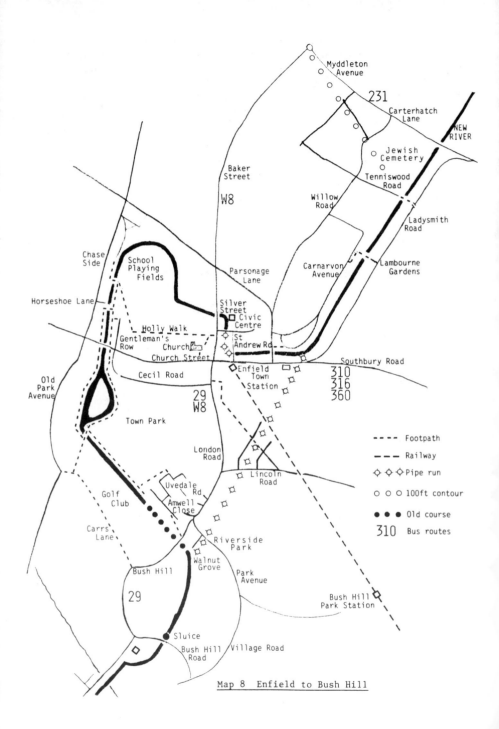

Map 8  Enfield to Bush Hill

44

*Enfield to Bush Hill* (Map 8)

From the footbridge at the end of Tenniswood Road, the New River continues south alongside Ladysmith Road and it is crossed by another footbridge from Lambourne Gardens leading to Carnarvon Avenue. On reaching Southbury Road the New River lies behind a wooden fence. Here it enters pipes which take it almost due south for three-quarters of a mile to re-enter the old course behind houses at the corner of Bush Hill with Park Avenue. The course of the pipe-run can be recognised on the surface because for most of its length there is a strip of allotments and open land over it; see it, for instance, by the car park behind the cinema, from the footpath between Chalkwell Park Avenue and Lyndhurst Gardens, and alongside Walnut Grove.

On the south side of Southbury Road, immediately opposite the entry to the pipes, can be seen some control valves which can adjust the volume of water entering the pipes; the old course of the New River round Enfield – the horseshoe loop – has been maintained and the Thames Water Authority has agreed to supply a small flow of water to the loop as an amenity. The horseshoe loop runs westwards along the north side of Southbury Road as far as St. Andrew Road. From here, where it turns northwards at the corner of Silver Street, it has been covered over to form a public car park and it emerges at Churchbury Lane to form an ornamental pond in front of the Civic Centre.

Enfield Parish Church stands nearby and a report in 1926 records that a gravestone there bears the epitaph:

"Here lies John White who day by day
On river works did use much clay,
Is now himself turning that way
If not to clay yet dust will come,
Which to preserve takes little room,
Although enclosed in this great tomb.
I served the New River Company as Surveyor
from Ladyday 1691 to Midsummer 1723." (22)

I have not been able to locate this grave.

A cast iron bridge over the Horseshoe Loop by River View, Enfield.

A picture postcard of Enfield c 1930 The New River in Enfield Town park.

From the Civic Centre the horseshoe loop turns westwards to flow under Silver Street and then runs alongside a track leading to the Civic Centre's private car park. Here it turns north and flows on three sides of a school playing field until it reaches Parsonage Gardens.   From the end of this road a footpath called River View crosses the water twice over attractive iron bridges, and passes Horseshoe Lane which is opposite 'The Crown and Horseshoes'.   Charles Lamb lived near here in 87, and later in 89, Chase Side.   Continue down River View to Gentlemans Row;  number 17, Clarendon Cottage, is where Charles Lamb and his sister, Mary, lodged with Mrs. Leisham in 1825 and again in 1827 (see page 22).   The river flows under Church Street into Enfield Town Park where it widens to form a lake with an island in it. Here the banks are strengthened with old railway sleepers so this must have been relatively recent renovation work.   At the southern end of the Park the loop turns eastwards under a footbridge and continues to the boundary where the water flows away to waste.   Walk up the path alongside the eastern boundary of the Park to an alleyway leading to Uvedale Road.   Turn right and follow the road round to Amwell Close.   The New River used to run at the back of the gardens of the houses on the south west side of the road, separating them from the golf course.   The course was abandoned when three lines of pipes were laid between Southbury Road and Bush Hill some time before 1926;  in October, 1940, the pipes were damaged by enemy action and a local resident recalls that the Pioneer Corps had to dig out the old course to re-establish the flow through the horseshoe loop.   When eventually the old course was filled in again, the householders in Amwell Close and Whitethorn Gardens were offered the land as an extension to their gardens.

From Amwell Close a footpath leads to Bush Hill.   The New River used to reach Bush Hill where Riverdale Court now stands and it ran up what is now the drive to No. 3a, Bush Hill and under the new house to link up with the present course. Walk down to the corner of Bush Hill and turn right into Park Avenue.   A short distance along on the left is Riverside Park and a sports field covering the southern end of the pipe-run under Enfield.   On the right-hand side is Walnut Grove with a strip of allotment on the eastern side of it.   At the top of Walnut Grove is a pair of iron gates and the place where the pipes re-enter the New River can be seen beyond them.

*Bush Hill to the North Circular Road* (Map 9)

The Sluice House, Bush Hill, beside Bush Hill Road.

In Bush Hill Road a sluice house spans the New River as it passes under the road and runs alongside the large house in which Hugh Myddelton lived during its construction; the present house accommodates the Halliwick School for Physically Handicapped Children. Just beyond this is the embankment replacing the Bush Hill Frame which originally carried the channel over Salmons Brook in a 666 foot lead trough which reached a height of 24 feet. A bridge was built over the brook and this was replaced in 1682 by an arch which is there today; a short cul-de-sac off Park Drive called Clarendon Way approaches Salmons Brook on the north-west of the New River — the garden at the end is privately owned. The arch, which is now supported by timber buttresses, carries a coat of arms and the inscription "This Arch was Rebuilt in the Yeare 1682, Honourable Henry Earle of Clarendon being Govr". An eighteenth Century engraving of the arch shows a plaque with the inscription "The Frame and Lead was raised one foot higher AD 1725". (see page 21).

47

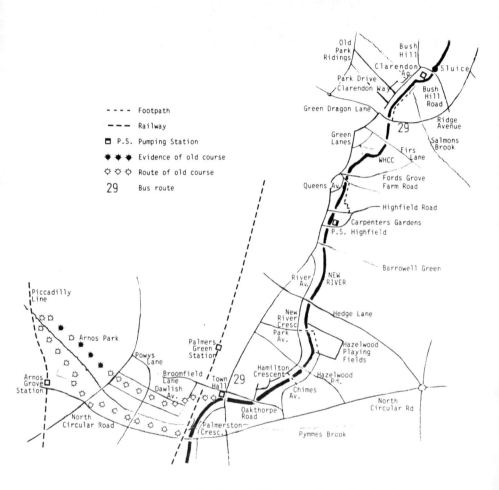

Footpath
Railway
P.S. Pumping Station
Evidence of old course
Route of old course
29 Bus route

Old Park Ridings
Bush Hill
Clarendon Av.
Sluice
Park Drive
Clarendon Way
Bush Hill Road
Green Dragon Lane
Ridge Avenue
29
Green Lanes
Salmons Brook
Firs Lane
WHCC
Fords Grove Farm Road
Queens Av.
Highfield Road
Carpenters Gardens
P.S. Highfield
Barrowell Green
River Av.
NEW RIVER
New River Cresc
Hedge Lane
Park Av.
Hazelwood Playing Fields
Palmers Green Station
Hamilton Crescent
Hazelwood Rd.
Piccadilly Line
Arnos Park
Powys Lane
Broomfield Lane
Town Hall
29
Chimes Av.
Arnos Grove Station
Dawlish Av.
North Circular Rd
North Circular Road
Oakthorpe Road
Palmerston Cresc.
Pymmes Brook

Map 9  Bush Hill to the North Circular Road

48

Clarendon Arch, Bush Hill in 1956. The wall at the top has now been removed
and the top plaque turned to face the road.

The top of the arch can be seen from Bush Hill and on this is a stone bearing an
inscription facing the road: "This Bank of Earth was raised and formed to support
the channel of the New River. And the Frame of Timber and Lead which served that
purpose 173 years was removed and taken away. MDCCLXXXVI. Peter Holford
Esquire Governor". It seems clear, therefore, that as the frame was replaced by the
embankment in 1786 which was 173 years after its completion, work on building the
frame must have continued into 1613, the year the New River was opened through to
Islington.

The embankment extends as far as Ridge Avenue and is clothed in grass with
some attractive trees alongside the water. The south-eastern aspect of the embankment can be seen from a footpath which leads from Ridge Avenue to tennis courts
close to the other end of the Clarendon Arch over Salmons Brook; this end is less
ornate than that by Clarendon Way.

Approaching Ridge Avenue, on the left bank, is one of the new cranes recently
installed by Thames Water for lifting maintenance boats into and out of the water;
these are mainly for weed-cutting and several cranes have been erected along the
course. Crossing under Ridge Avenue the New River runs behind houses to emerge
at the Winchmore Hill Cricket Club ground in Firs Lane. Its winding course can be
glimpsed from Beaulieu Gardens and from the end of Blenheim Close. It then runs
alongside Green Lanes behind the car park of Capital House; on old maps a branch
in the water channel is shown approaching Green Lanes for about twenty yards but
of this there is now no sign on the surface. At about this point is the entry to an
easement channel, a pipe to take surplus water around the Fords Grove and Farm

Road bridges, returning it to the River under the private car park behind 'Charter House', Queens Avenue.

Fords Grove and Farm Road cross the New River by narrow bridges; immediately over the Farm Road bridge on the right is a footpath which lies beside the water until just before it joins Highfield Road. Turn right to the narrow twin bridge by which is displayed a Metropolitan Water Board notice quoting the Motor Car Acts of 1896 and 1903 regarding the weights of vehicles allowed to cross. Turn left down Green Lanes to the corner of Carpenters Gardens where stands Highfield Pumping Station. This pumping station was closed in 1962, but the pump has continued raising water for the New River intermittently since; it could well be retained after the diversion of the New River at Maidens Brook to supply water to the channel as an amenity and in times of drought. On the wall facing the main entrance can be seen a hinged metal plate, now rusting. A workshop was housed at this corner of the building and this allowed long lengths of metal to be machined; around the corner to the right a tube is built into the wall so that long pipes may be offered up to the power tools inside.

Just beyond Barrowell Green turn left into River Avenue and continue into New River Crescent. At Park Avenue turn left over the footbridge into Hazelwood Playing Fields and follow the New River southwards; cross Hazelwood Lane into Chimes Avenue, take the first footpath on the right over the New River and turn left into Hamilton Crescent. At the junction at the end turn left into Riverway which leads to Oakthorpe Road. The playing fields on the east of the New River are school property. A narrow footpath alongside the southern edge of the channel from the

The New River loop in Arnos Park, 1819, now abandoned.

bridge in Oakthorpe Road does not continue very far. The New River then crosses under Green Lanes where it can be seen alongside Southgate Town Hall. An embankment at the back of the houses in Palmerston Crescent carries the channel over Pymmes Brook and extends as far as the North Circular Road, eliminating the old loop to the west.

From Southgate Town Hall the 100ft contour crosses Powys Lane near Dawlish Avenue, but there is no trace of the old course until, in Arnos Park, a line of shrubs and trees half way up the slope between Pymmes Brook and the northern boundary of the park clearly indicates the position of the old loop. Just beyond this is a clump of trees with a ditch running through them. The loop must have crossed Pymmes Brook near where the Picadilly Line viaduct now stands, and returned to the present course at Bowes Park where it reaches the North Circular Road.

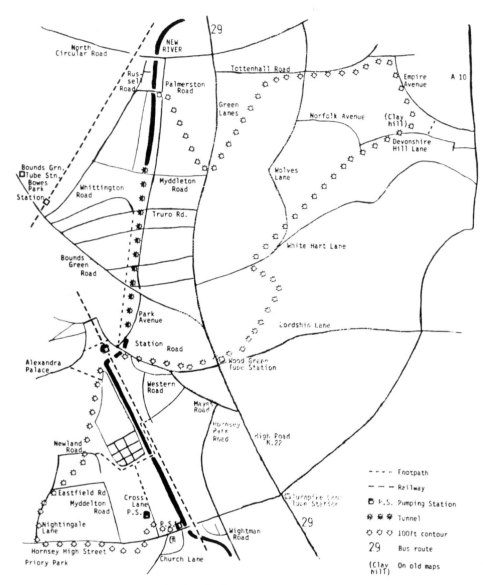

Map 10   The North Circular Road to Hornsey

52

*North Circular Road to Hornsey* (Map 10)

 The North Circular Road offers an interesting view of the influence of the Road's development on the New River. On the south side the pavement rises some eight feet above the level of the road in an arc. At its summit was until recently the brick side of a bridge over the New River; this has now been replaced by a fence and the New River starts a few yards south of it. On the north side the New River on its embankment terminates with a weed-catching structure across it, and it seems clear that when the North Circular Road was enlarged in 1962/63, the nearby railway bridge made it impracticable to eliminate the hump-back bridge by raising the road on either side of the New River; the alternative was to lower the road, taking the river under the road in a 'U-bend' conduit. Russell Road and the old Roche Laboratories building dated 1896 at its corner were once at the level of Bowes Road though vehicular entry to Russell Road from the North Circular Road is now impossible. The weed-catcher at the entry to the conduit is needed to prevent rubbish from collecting under the road.

The North Circular Road at Bowes Road. Until 1962 the road crossed the New River at the same level as the pavement seen on the far side.

 Walk down Russell Road. The New River soon disappears behind houses but it can be seen from the end of Granville Road and again when it passes under Whittington Road. From here it is apparent that the New River is in a cutting and, on reaching Myddelton Road, it enters a tunnel. This tunnel, 700 yards long and 14 feet wide built in 1852, made redundant the old loop to the east out as far as Edmonton. From Myddelton Road the strip of land over the tunnel has no buildings upon it. Walk east from the northern tunnel mouth, turn right into Palmerston Road and continue to Truro Road. From here there is an open space, owned by Thames Water but leased to the London Borough of Haringey, which stretches to the southern mouth at Park Avenue.

A snow scene of the New
River at Wolves Lane,
Edmonton, in 1905. This
section has been abandoned
and built over.

The old course swung eastwards past the Church of St. Michael at Bowes to cross Palmerston Road but it has been built over and is difficult to recognise. The 100ft contour crosses High Road, N.22, near the junction with Myddelton Road, and runs eastwards alongside Tottenhall Road as far as Empire Avenue. It then swings south and then west again, skirting a small hill referred to on old maps as Clay Hill, Edmonton. Just south of Devonshire Hill Lane traces of the old course of the New River can be identified, for instance near the top of the footpath linking Devonshire Hill Lane with White Hart Lane (near the junction with Devonshire Road). It then seemed to course across the end of Norfolk Avenue, but it can no longer be recognised where it crosses the New River Sports Ground – the name identifying the site with the past – Wolves Lane and the recreation ground alongside White Hart Lane. It must have crossed White Hart Lane near the old school towards Ewart Grove and its old course could have been along the curved garden backs behind Ewart Grove but it seems more likely that it occupied what is now the open green strip between Stuart Crescent and the High Road. The 100ft contour re-crosses the High Road north of Wood Green Station to rejoin the present course of the New River at the south end of the tunnel.

The tunnel mouth can be seen from Station Road, near Alexandra Palace BR Station. There is a footbridge over the railway just north of the station and this leads to the entrance to Alexandra Park. Approaching the park there is a small car park on the left and leading from it is a path into a Nature Reserve. At the bottom of the hill a good view of the New River, as it passes beneath the railway, and the filter beds may be obtained. The New River now runs parallel to the railway line but the old course veered westwards alongside the grounds of Alexandra Palace, crossing Moselle Brook which ran in the valley to the south of the Palace; the brook now runs underground. It is possible to walk through the Palace grounds but a better view of the present

The New River at Clay Hill, Edmonton, near Devonshire Mill Lane. Now abandoned.

course is achieved by returning over the railway to Station Road and crossing the New River.    To the left of the bridge is Wood Green Common with a Public Baths in the far corner.    Walk down Western Road to the footpath on the right-hand side, leading under the railway line, and emerging beside the New River and its filter beds with an excellent view of Alexandra Palace on the hill beyond.    Follow the footpath southwards and over the New River; just beyond the footbridge the path branches. The left branch takes you to Cross Lane where, on the right, stands Campsbourne well and pumping station (with a preservation order on it).    Continue up to Hornsey High Street and on the left is Hornsey pumping station.    The New River crosses under the road and beneath the railway line.

To trace the old course, return to Cross Lane – a narrow entrance with the Great Northern Railway Tavern on the corner – and go back to the footpath junction. Turn left and follow the path round by the filter beds to Newland Road.    The 100ft contour runs down Myddelton Road and swings right in the area of Eastfield Road. Myddelton and Campsbourne Roads have been blocked half-way down but walk along Newland Road which leads into Nightingale Lane.    The road slopes down as far as Eastfield Road and old maps suggest that the New River joined Nightingale Lane here and followed it down to Priory Park where it swung east and ran along the south side of Hornsey High Street towards the church.    Here it crossed the High Street and ran under Cross Lane to the site of the present pumphouse.    At one time I had the impression that the old course could be seen in the churchyard on the south and east of the Church running from a brick wall with a worn, unreadable, stone plaque on it (perhaps a bridge?) across to the corner of the churchyard beside Church Lane.    Here there is what appears to be another bridge and there is a hump in the High Street where the old course could have crossed under the road.    Although this conjecture is not supported by old maps, the channel certainly ran through part of a churchyard; a reference to Hornsey in an 1880 publication states:  "the New River would now be sought for in vain; its course was diverted, and this portion filled up with the vestigia of a London cemetery." (18)

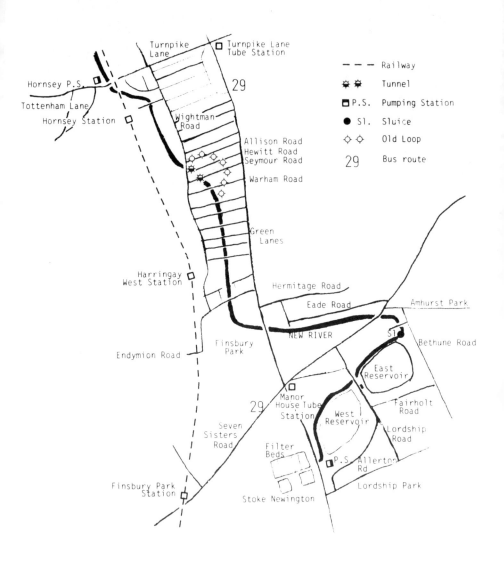

Map 11   Hornsey to Stoke Newington

*Hornsey to Stoke Newington*  (Map 11)

The New River crosses under High Street, Hornsey, at its junction with Tottenham Lane; it can be seen at the back of the flats in Denmark Road and again from the bridge on Hampden Road.  Its present course enters a cutting behind the houses in Wightman Road, where a steep hill rises opposite the end of Allison Road, and it enters a 200 yard tunnel, 7 feet in diameter, under Wightman Road to emerge at the side of New River House in Seymour Road.  Previously the New River skirted this hill on which stood a Tudor mansion until 1750; Harringay House was built on the site in 1796 and this was demolished in 1885-6 to make way for the present housing estate. The old course ran eastwards, to the north of Allison Road, to about half-way along the road, swinging south to rejoin the present course near Warham Road.

The Stoke Newington Reservoirs and Pumping Station.

From here the New River runs southwards between the houses to enter Finsbury Park where it swings to the east and leaves the park under Green Lanes. It runs alongside Eade Road and crosses under Seven Sisters Road near the junction with Amhurst Park. A short distance down Bethune Road, on the right, is a cul-de-sac which crosses the New River and affords a good view of a sluice house and the reservoirs. Lordship Road runs between the East and West Reservoirs and a building beside the East Reservoir bears a stone inscribed "These reservoirs the property of the New River Company were begun in the year 1830 and completed in the year 1833 under the direction of Mr. William Chadwell Mylne, their engineer. Robert Percy Smith Esquire, Governor." This building is all that remains of the 1830 pumping station. The West Reservoir was completed in 1831 and its banks were faced with stones from the old London Bridge which was being demolished at the time. The old pumping station on Green Lanes was built to look like a castle by William Chadwell Mylne in 1855 in order not to offend local property owners. Notice the surmounted columns on either side of Lordship Park on the right of the pumphouse which looks like the entrance to a property of distinction.

The large red building lying back from the road behind the 'castle' is the primary filter house. Opposite the reservoirs, on the west side of Green Lanes, are the filter beds built in 1852. The present course of the New River terminates at Stoke Newington though much of the old course may be traced beyond here.

Sluice House Tavern

New River

New Sluice House 1841

Filter Beds

(Wilberforce Road)

Bank of Clay "Boarded River"

Kings Road

Queens Road

Blackstock Road

Gypsy Lane

(Mountgrove Road)

Highbury Vale

New River

(Riversdale Road)

Highbury Park Tavern

Quadrant Road North

(Highbury Quadrant)

Highbury New Park

Green Lanes

Quadrant Road South

Map 12 "The Boarded River"

Based on Ordnance Survey 1869; Published 1871
(Present road names in parentheses)

59

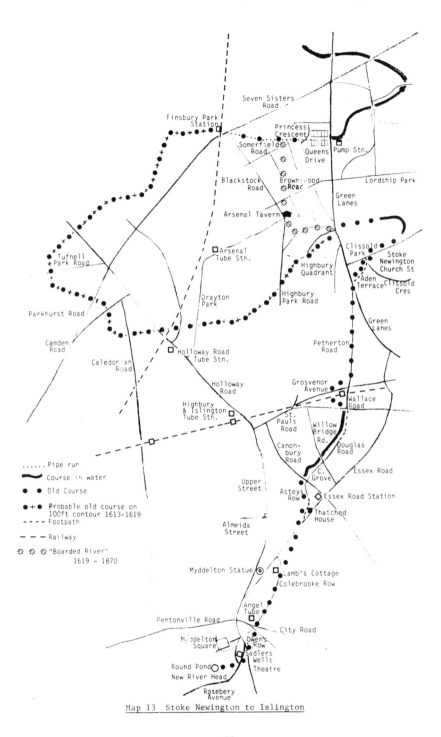

Map 13  Stoke Newington to Islington

60

*Stoke Newington to Islington* (Maps 12 & 13)

The old course may be determined by reference to the 100ft contour and to old maps of the area, particularly a map of a survey carried out in 1869.

The New River was originally dug due west on the 100ft contour, past the filter beds, crossed Seven Sisters Road near where Finsbury Park Station is now, and swung south near the junction of Holloway Road with Tufnell Park Road. It then crossed Parkhurst Road and Caledonian Road and it turned north west by Drayton Park Station, along Highbury Quadrant and into Clissold Park. The loop was cut short in 1619 when a 462 foot aqueduct was constructed, crossing Stroud Green Brook — a tributary of Hackney Brook — between Seven Sisters Road and Riversdale Road. Along the route of the old loop, particularly between Queens Drive and Finsbury Park Station, can be seen a number of metal plates in the road and on pavements marked 'N.R.' and some marked 'M.W.B.'

Many of the roads in this area have been blocked to prevent through traffic. Enter Princess Crescent from Queens Drive and on the right is a car park serving a block of flats. From here the 'Castle' pumping station can be seen across the filter beds and in a straight line from the nearby fence, across a green area, the old course is indicated by iron markers; on either side of the gate onto the grass is a pair of iron posts fifteen feet apart, each marked "TRACK MWB" and on the path near Princess Crescent is a metal plate inscribed "T MWB". A double row of metal studs cross the corner of the school playground and on the wall opposite, at the corner of Queens Drive and Somerfield Road, is a cast iron plate marked "NRC PIPE TRACK"; a similar plate is on the wall just round the corner in Somerfield Road. From here, in the line of the pipe-run, can be seen a clear space between the backs of houses, terminating in a domed building. In Wilberforce Road — in the course of this clear strip — is Luesley's Hotel on the east side with a "MWB PIPE TRACK" plate on the wall and opposite it is Central Park Hotel with, on the wall by the road, two plates inscribed "NRC PIPE TRACK" each with an arrow marking the limits of the New River Company land; they are about twenty-two feet apart. There are two MWB posts in the hotel car park and another "NRC PIPE TRACK" plate can be seen on the east side of Finsbury Park Road. From here the track leads to the domed building. This is Nexus House, on the corner of Seven Sisters Road and Blackstock Road, and in its basement I have seen a large metal pipe continuing the straight course from Queens Drive.

It would be reasonable to assume that the pipes are laid along the old course of the New River — they are on the 100ft contour — and this would be reasonable as the Company owned the land. Contemporary maps of the area suggest that the Sluice House Tavern and the 'New Sluice House', where the New River was turned south in 1619 onto the 466 foot timber aqueduct known locally at the time as the 'Boarded River', must have stood to the south of the corner of Somerfield Road and Wilberforce Road. From here it ran due south, passing what is now Mountgrove Road (it was Gipsy Lane) and people now living in the area describe the Arsenal Tavern on the corner with Blackstock Road as 'the old sluice house'. Although this is a prevalent view there is no evidence on old maps that there was ever a sluice house at this end of the aqueduct. The 'boarded river' then turned eastwards and ran along Riversdale Road where it rejoined the original course. Crossing Green Lanes it entered Clissold Park by an old stone hut, which is still there, and crossed to the lake along an easily recognised route. The lake itself is clearly part of the New River as it coursed north-eastwards and turned south-east, but where it reached Stoke Newington Church Street and ran south-west alongside it the channel is obliterated. A short length of fencing, different from that on either side of it, seems to be the point at which the New River swung south towards Clissold Crescent, crossing under the road.

On the right of Clissold Crescent (shown on old maps as Park Lane) are railings at one end of a strip of allotments; a metal plate attached to them records "The Park Lane Bridge was demolished and the road widened June 1931". The curve of the allotments clearly indicates the old course. Walk beside them along the footpath, Aden Terrace, and notice the suggestion of an embankment on the left-hand side. At the end cross Green Lanes into Petherton Road. The New River continued down Petherton Road along what is now a wide central reservation running nearly the entire length of the road. Standing at the southern end of this reservation it is apparent that the road level drops as it passes Grosvenor Avenue and Canonbury Station, and it rises again towards the end of Wallace Road where it joins St. Paul's Road. Old maps show that the channel turned, along the 100ft contour, in a loop to the west. It swung right at Beresford Terrace and continued behind the houses to cross Grosvenor Avenue near where there is now a new block of flats (Spring Gardens). There is a terrace of old properties along the south of Grosvenor Avenue but in two places there is apparently newer building. One is at No.127, Eve Court, and the other at Nos.139 and 139a; Michael Graubart has counted the houses and compared it with an old map which shows a gap where 139 and 139a now stand. There is now no indication of where the channel crossed the railway line but beyond it, opposite the 'gap', is a curved narrow space between houses in a position consistent with the course shown on old maps along which the New River reached St. Paul's Road at the corner with Wallace Road. (32)

At the bottom of Wallace Road cross St. Paul's Road to an un-named pathway opposite with a strip of shrubs and trees on the right. A few yards along here we see another stretch of the old course still in water and we can follow it for some distance. The path opens into Douglas Road (older maps show Douglas Road continuing to St. Paul's Road but recent building work has shortened it). Cross Willow Bridge Road and continue by the water alongside Canonbury Grove on New River Walk. Half-way along there is a deviation in its course as it passes a small brick hut said to have belonged to the Metropolitan Water Board.  From Canonbury Road the rest of the old course is almost dry but beside Asteys Row there is a children's play area and paddling pools and New River Walk extends to Essex Road where a public toilet has been built, over the old course, beside the Thatched Cottage public house.

Remnant of the New River by New River Walk, Canonbury Grove.
The most southerly section of the abandoned course still in water.

It is difficult to trace the course from here but we are helped by Pugin and Brayley who, writing in 1919 about the Thatched House, Islington, at the angle of Lower Street and the footpath leading to Canonbury record "Near this spot also, in its course southward, the New River is arched over and runs underground for upwards of 200 yards, till it again emerges near the top of Colebrook-row." (25).  Here the old course can be recognised in the strip along the right-hand side of Colebrooke Row. An LCC plaque on the first house on the right records that Charles Lamb once lived here (see page 22) and the New River certainly ran "close to the foot of the house" but the ginger-beer factory next door mentioned by Lucas seems now to be a private lock-up garage.   It continues between Colebrooke Row and Duncan Terrace as far as City Road and Goswell Road.   Near here, on Islington Green, stands a statue of Sir Hugh Myddelton which is worth a visit.   Myddelton's house, built c.1595, stands a short distance up Upper Street on the corner with Almeida Street.

The old course crossed the roads, and the forecourt of the petrol filling station at the angle of the two roads, and ran down the right side of Owen's Row.   Owen's Row is now almost eliminated but the name can be seen low on a wall beside the car park;   the Dame Alice Owen Building, housing the City University Department of Optometry and Visual Science, is a recent building across the route.   A small remnant of the road joins St. John Street where the New River crossed to what is now Rosebery Avenue; early maps of this area show the New River running along the south side of Sadlers Wells Theatre to enter the round pond beside where the TWA Laboratories now stand. Opposite the theatre, on a 1753 map is marked "Tunbridge Wells" and on a 1799 map the same spot is marked "Islington Spa".

The course from Colebrooke Row to New River Head was covered over in 1861 and the Petherton Road section was covered over in 1868-70.

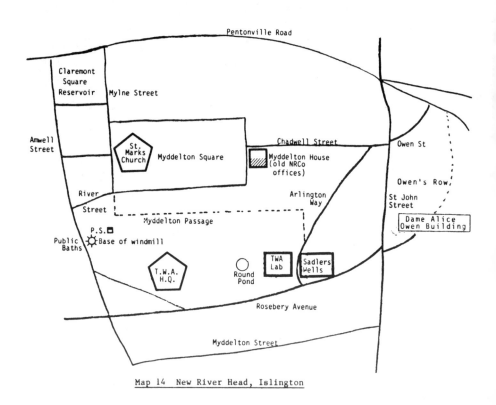

Map 14  New River Head, Islington

*New River Head, Islington* (Map 14)

At New River Head there is a tiny round pond and around the Headquarters of the Thames Water Authority can be seen remnants of the old reservoir which was the termination of the New River. On the first floor of this building is the 17th century Oak Room which was the original Room for meetings of the New River Company. Fitted out by Grinling Gibbons, and with a ceiling painting of William III by Henry Cooke, the room was purchased from the New River Company by the Metropolitan Water Board in 1904 and fitted into the new building when it was built in 1920.

Between the round pond and Sadlers Wells Theatre is the T.W.A. Laboratory. High on the wall is the Metropolitan Water Board crest bearing the same motto as on the Seal of the New River Company, which it absorbed, and two hands, in place of the original one, sprinkling water. Two figures on either side represent a boy pouring water from a pot and a girl holding a hose-pipe. On a publication by the M.W.B. in 1953 an old man appeared in place of the boy. The eight drops of water represent the eight water companies which formed the M.W.B.

The base of the original windmill built in 1709 to pump water into the 'New Pond' – now the covered reservoir in Claremont Square – can be seen from the TWA car park entrance in Amwell Street. Behind the windmill is the pumphouse, built in 1768 to house the Smeaton steam engine. This was replaced in 1787 by a Boulton and Watt engine but the pumping is now done electrically.

Myddelton Square may be reached from Amwell Street by going down River Street. On the right at the entrance to the square is Myddelton Passage, a pathway skirting the back of the site of New River Head, emerging in Arlington Way opposite Sadlers Wells Theatre. To the north Mylne Street leads to Claremont Square dominated by the covered reservoir. On the east side of the square, on the corner of Chadwell Street, is Myddelton House, until recently the offices of the New River Company Ltd. This continued to be responsible for the property owned by the Company, although its New River services had been taken over by the Metropolitan Water Board in 1904 and by the Thames Water Authority in 1974. The offices were lined with countless prints of the New River dating back to the 17th Century and a four foot length of elm pipe which once distributed the water to London homes served as an umbrella stand. On a mantelpiece stood a clock, the movement inserted into the bore of a three-inch section of elm pipe. These offices are now closed and the documents transferred to archives.

Myddelton Square was laid out by William Chadwell Mylne, Chief Engineer to the New River Company from 1811 to 1863, and he built St. Marks Church in the Square in 1827. On the wall at the back of the Church is a plaque recording the death of Sir Hugh Myddelton on 10 December, 1631 with the words "Engineer, Goldsmith and Public Benefactor. He brought Fresh Water to London."

"New River Head, Islington. A cartoon by Cruickshank, Aug.13 1796"

# REFERENCES AND BIBLIOGRAPHY

(1) History of the New River by R.E. Morris, M.I.Mech.E., 1934. Northern Area Engineer, Metropolitan Water Board. Typescript.

(2) London – or Interesting Memorials of its Rise, Progress & Present State by Sholto & Reuben Percy. Vol. 1. T. Boys, London 1824 pp 133-140

(3) The Gentleman's Magazine and Historical Chronicle, Vol.37, 1767, p.337

(4) Sir Hugh Myddelton and the New River by G.C.F. Berry, M.A., 1957. Published by the Honourable Society of Cymmrodorion.

(5) History of the New River, 1983. Thames Water Authority

(6) Industrial Archaeology in Enfield, 1971. Research Report No. 2. Enfield Archaeological Society.

(7) An Encyclopaedia of London, Edited by William Kent. Dent, London, 1937

(8) The History of London from its foundation by the Romans to the present time by William Maitland. 1739, p.629.

(9) National History and Views of London and its Environs, Vol.II, 1835 Ed: C.F. Partington

(10) The Navigation of the River Lee (1190–1790) by J.G.L. Burnby and M. Parker. 1978. Occasional Paper New Series No.36. Edmonton Hundred Historical Society.

(11) The Gentleman's Magazine and Historical Chronicle, Vol.23, 1753, pp.114–116

(12) Some Descriptive Notes on the New River Head by G.F. Stringer. Metropolitan Water Board, October 1927

(13) The Gentleman's Magazine and Historical Chronicle, Vol.63 (Part I) 1793, p.225

(14) Wren's London by Eric de Mare. 1975, p.38. The Folio Society

(15) The Gentleman's Magazine and Historical Chronicle, Vol.19, 1749, pp.435–437

(16) Ibid, Vol.54 (Part II) 1784, (a) p.643; (b) p.723; (c) pp.803–805; (d) Vol.58 (Part I), 1788, p.460; (e) Vol.57 (Part I), 1787, p.361; (f) Vol.68 (Part I), 1798 p.805.

(17) Essays of Elia by Charles Lamb – Newspapers thirty-five years ago, p.295. London, Macmillan & Co. 1929.

(18) Old and New Views of London by Walter Thornbury. c 1880

(19) A Wanderer in London by E.V. Lucas. 1913, p.143. Methuen

(20) Essays of Elia by Charles Lamb – Amicus Redivivus, p.281. London, Macmillan & Co., 1929

(21) Charles Dickens: London Guide for 1879 – facsimile reprint – London, Howard Baker, 1972.

(22) The Romance of the New River: Twentieth Annual Report to the Metropolitan Water Board, 1926, by Sir Alexander Houston

(23) History with a Sketch-Book by Donald Maxwell. Bodley Head, London 1926

(24) The Fringe of London by Gordon S. Maxwell, illustrated by Donald Maxwell. Cecil Palmer, London 1925

(25) A Series of Views in Islington and Pentonville by Augustus Pugin and Edward Wedlake Brayley. London, 1819

(26) Hydraulia; An Historical and Descriptive Account of the Waterworks of London by William Matthews. London, 1835

(27) The Water Supply of London. Ed. S.D. Askew, Metropolitan Water Board, 1961

(28) Sir Hugh Myddelton; Entrepreneur and Engineer by J.W. Gough. Clarendon Press, Oxford. 1964

(29) The New River. The Boy's Own Paper; Vol. VII, No.323, pp.395-399, Saturday 21 March, 1885

(30) Personal communication from H.M. Fletcher, Dealer in Rare Books, London, WC2
(31) A Tour through the Whole Island of Great Britain by Daniel Defoe. London, 1724
(32) Michael Graubart; personal communication
(33) London's Water Supply 1903 – 1953. Compiled by L.J. Flowerdew and G.C.F. Berry. Metropolitan Water Board. 1953
(34) The New River – A Legal History by Bernard Rudden, Clarendon Press 1985
(35) A survey of London by John Stow. London 1598.

Further Reading

The British Metropolis in 1851: A Classified Guide to London. London, 1851
Supply of Water to the Metropolis. Illustrated London News, pp.521-23; 22 November, 1856
A Perambulation of Islington by Thomas Edlyne Tomkins. London, 1858
The Master Masons to the Crowns of Scotland and their works by Rev. Robert Scott Mylne. Scott & Ferguson & Burness & Co., Edinburgh 1893
Greater London by Ed. Walford. Vol.I. London 1898
London's Water Supply by Richard Sisley. Scientific Press, 1899
The Water Supply of London. 1949. Metrpolitan Water Board
Robert Mylne – Architect and Engineer – 1733-1811 by A.E. Richardson, Batsford, London, 1955
A History of London Life by R.J. Mitchell and M.D.R. Leys. Pelican Books, 1963
Sir Hugh Myddelton: Practical Idealist, by Patricia Braun. London 1980
Sir Hugh Myddelton – The First Mines Adventurer by Peter Naylor, Bulletin Peak District Mines Historical Society, Vol.8 No.1, pp.54-59; 1981
The Oak Room at New River Head. Thames Water Authority
An Historical Walk Along the New River by Mary Cosh, Islington Libraries, 1982.

## ADDRESSES


Thames Water, The Grange, Crossbrook Street, Waltham Cross, Herts.
(Waltham Cross (0992) 23611)

Lee Valley Regional Park Authority, Myddleton House, Bulls Cross, Enfield.
(Lea Valley (0992) 717711)

London Records Office and History Library, 40 Northampton Road, London, EC1
(01 633 7132)

# INDEX

The spelling of some names — notably that of Sir Hugh Myddelton — varies in different references to him.   I have chosen the spelling which appears to be most authentic for this index, though variations appear on some pages, especially in quotations from 17th and 18th Century documents.   I have adopted the spelling 'Lee' for the River, though Lea is a common alternative.

## *ACKNOWLEDGEMENTS*

The preparation of a booklet like this requires the help of many people and I record my gratitude to the individuals and bodies who have given so much assistance to me in the past few years.   I would mention particularly Frank Bamping who has collaborated so closely with me, especially with the literary references; the Shakespeare Institute of the University of Birmingham advised me on contemporary dramatic references.   Gordon Dodd, who has been studying the New River independently, shared his conclusions with me and has given me much valued help; I am indebted to him for the time he spent reading the proofs and for suggesting many amendments and changes in the text.   I have had extensive help from the Thames Water Authority, the New River Company Ltd., the reference librarians and local historians in the Counties and Boroughs through which the New River flows, and the London Records Office and History Library.   Many of the prints and early photographs were provided by Graham Dalling and are reproduced by permission of the Local History Department of the London Borough of Enfield.

I have had considerable help from my publisher, Alan Brewin, who has produced such an elegant volume from my manuscript, and has achieved a remarkable relationship between my numerous illustrations and maps and the text to which they refer.

I am very grateful to those who have written to me and sent me documents, particularly Peter J. Naylor, H.M. Fletcher, Lorna Middleton — a descendant of Sir Hugh — Michael Graubart who has studied in detail the old route from Stoke Newington to New River Head. The clock illustrated on page 9 was generously given to me by Leonard Whiskin. Their suggestions and advice have provided me with valuable sources for further research which has been incorporated into this second edition.

My wife, who walked the New River with me, gives me constant support.